Easy *Piano*

Hits from Broadway Musicals

Hal Leonard Europe
Distributed by Music Sales

Exclusive Distributors:
Music Sales Limited
8/9 Frith Street, London W1D 3JB, England.
Music Sales Pty Limited
120 Rothschild Avenue, Rosebery, NSW 2018, Australia.

Order No. HLE90000760
ISBN 0-7119-8248-1
This book © Copyright 2000 by Hal Leonard Europe.

Cover design by Michael Bell Design.
Photographs courtesy of Rex Features.
Printed in the USA.

Your Guarantee of Quality
As publishers, we strive to produce every book to
the highest commercial standards.
The book has been carefully designed to
minimise awkward page turns and
to make playing from it a real pleasure.
Throughout, the printing and binding have
been planned to ensure a sturdy, attractive publication
which should give years of enjoyment.
If your copy fails to meet our high standards,
please inform us and we will gladly replace it.

Music Sales' complete catalogue describes
thousands of titles and is available in
full colour sections by subject,
direct from Music Sales Limited.
Please state your areas of interest and send a
cheque/postal order for £1.50 for postage to:
Music Sales Limited,
Newmarket Road, Bury St. Edmunds, Suffolk
IP33 3YB, England.

www.musicsales.com

ALL I ASK OF YOU

from THE PHANTOM OF THE OPERA

Music by ANDREW LLOYD WEBBER
Lyrics by CHARLES HART
Additional Lyrics by RICHARD STILGOE

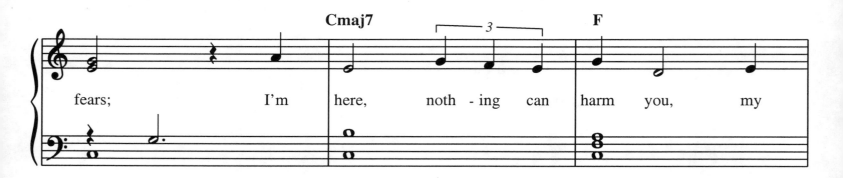

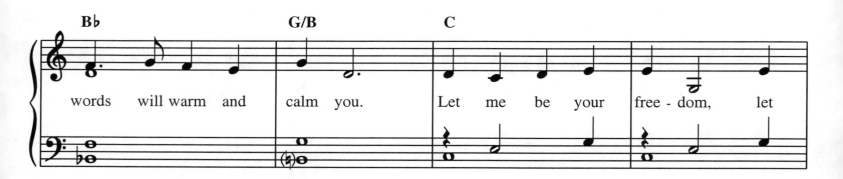

5

F   Bb   G/B   CHRISTINE: C

side you,   to   guard you and to   guide you.   Say   you

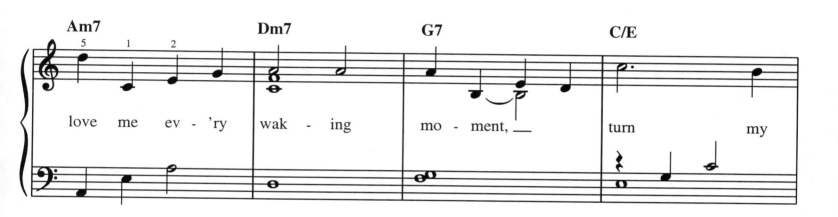

Am7   Dm7   G7   C/E

love me ev - 'ry   wak - ing   mo - ment, __   turn   my

Am/E   Dm7   G7

head   with   talk   of   sum - mer - time.

C   Am7   Dm7   G7

Say   you   need me with you   now   and   al - ways; __

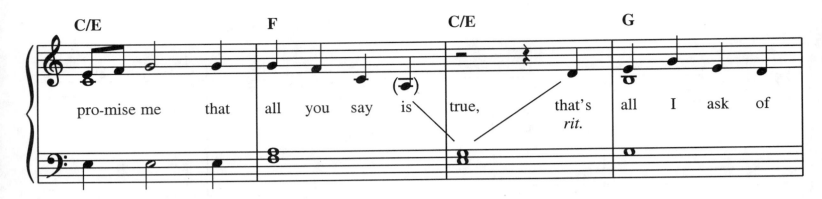

C/E **F** **C/E** **G**

pro-mise me that all you say is true, that's all I ask of
rit.

RAOUL:

C

mf
Let me be your shel - ter, let me be your light; you're
you.
a tempo

Cmaj7 **F** **B♭**

— *3* —

safe, no one will find you, your fears are far be -

CHRISTINE:

G/B **C**

hind you. All I want is free - dom, a world with no more

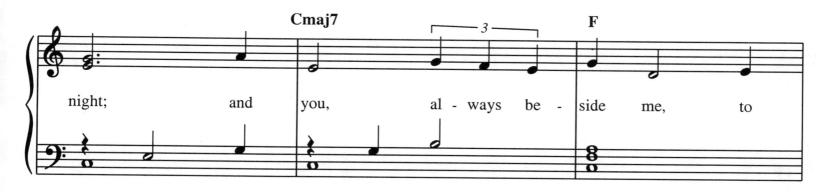

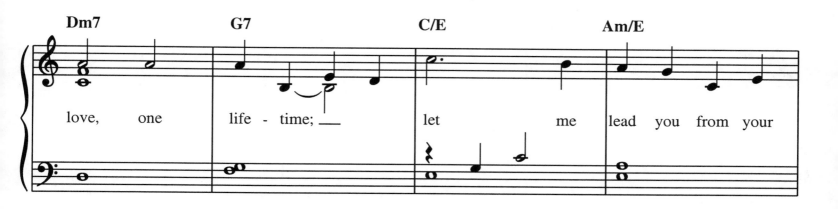

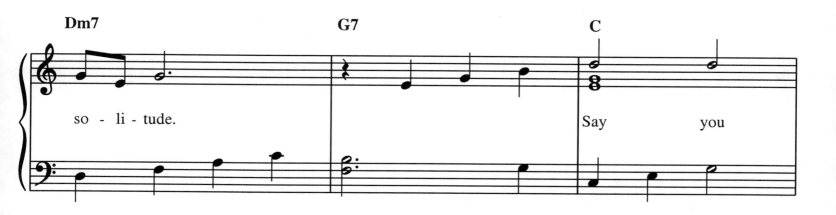

8

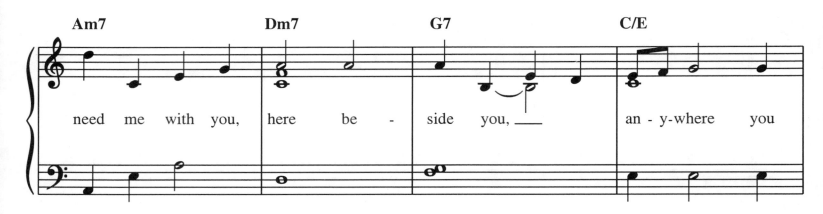

Am7   Dm7   G7   C/E

need me with you, here be - side you, _____ an - y-where you

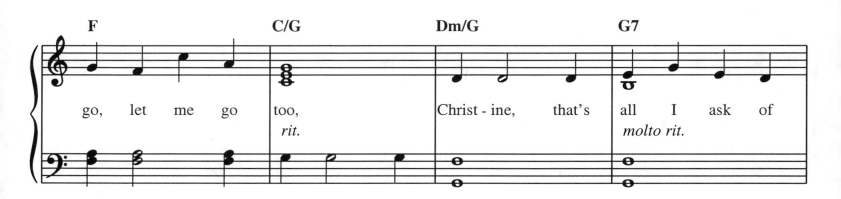

F   C/G   Dm/G   G7

go, let me go too, Christ - ine, that's all I ask of

rit.   *molto rit.*

CHRISTINE:

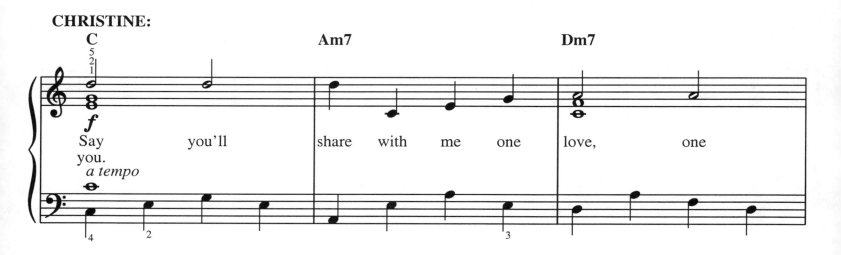

C   Am7   Dm7

f   Say you'll share with me one love, one

you.

a tempo

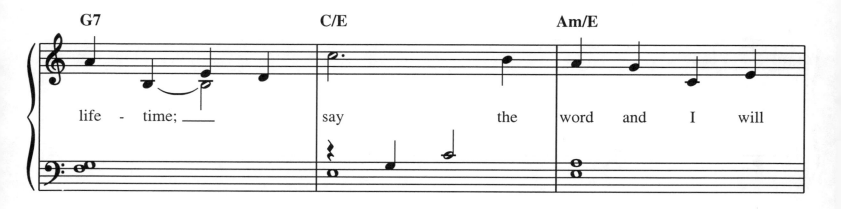

G7   C/E   Am/E

life - time; _____ say the word and I will

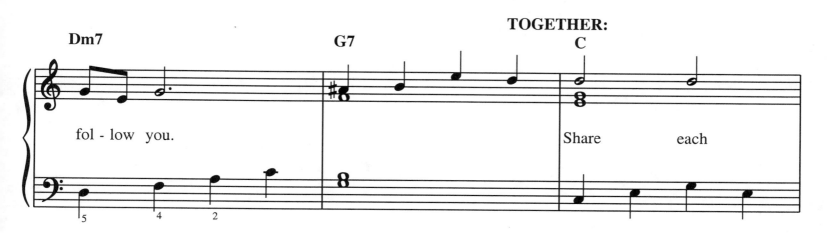

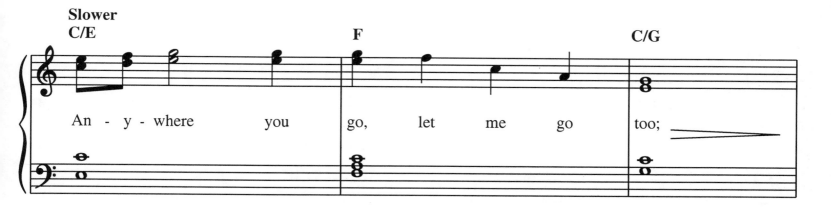

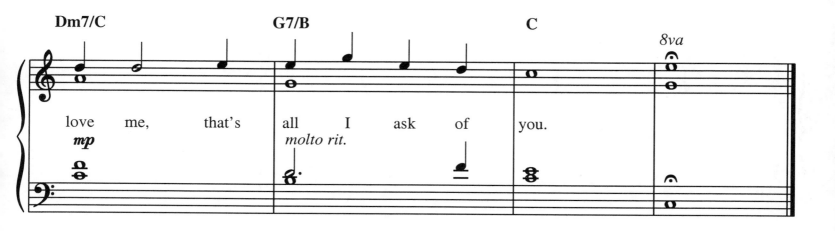

ANY DREAM WILL DO

from JOSEPH AND THE AMAZING TECHNICOLOR ® DREAMCOAT

Music by ANDREW LLOYD WEBBER
Lyrics by TIM RICE

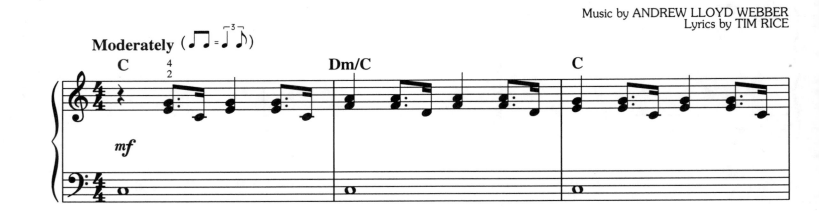

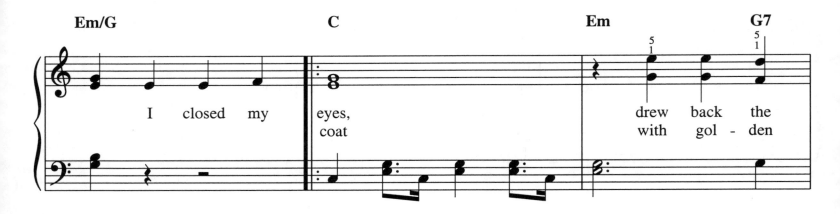

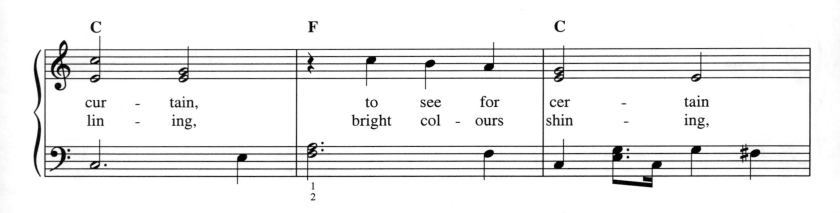

BEAUTY AND THE BEAST

from Walt Disney's BEAUTY AND THE BEAST: THE BROADWAY MUSICAL

Lyrics by HOWARD ASHMAN
Music by ALAN MENKEN

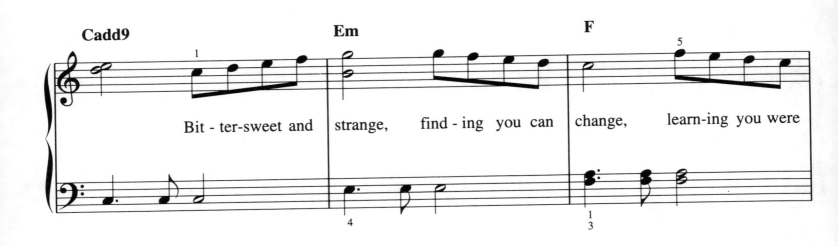

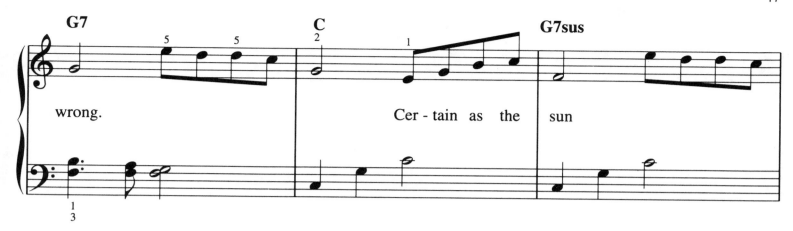

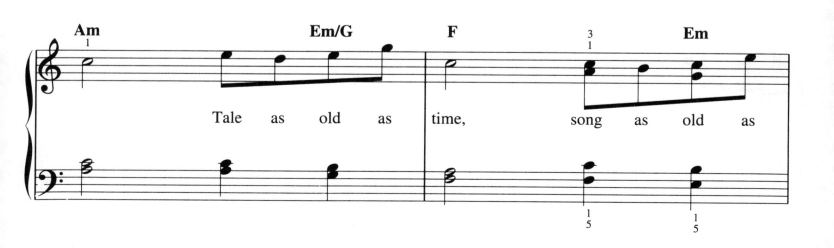

CAN'T HELP LOVIN' DAT MAN
from SHOW BOAT

Words by OSCAR HAMMERSTEIN II
Music by JEROME KERN

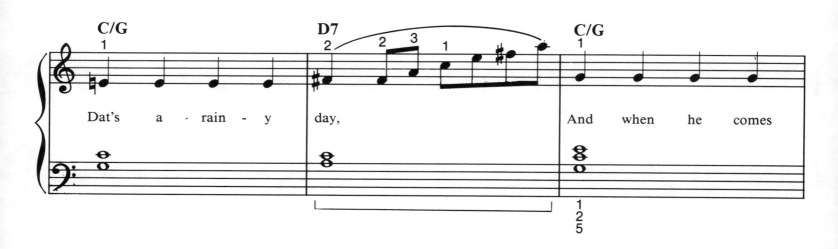

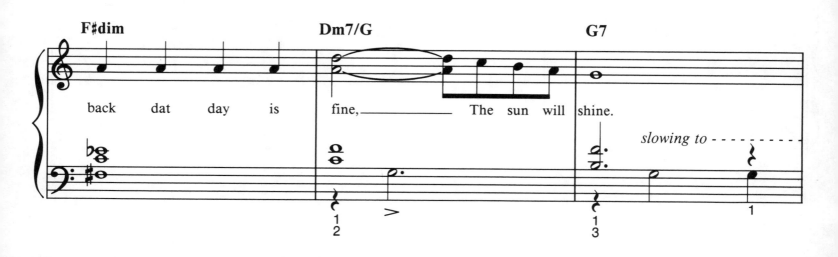

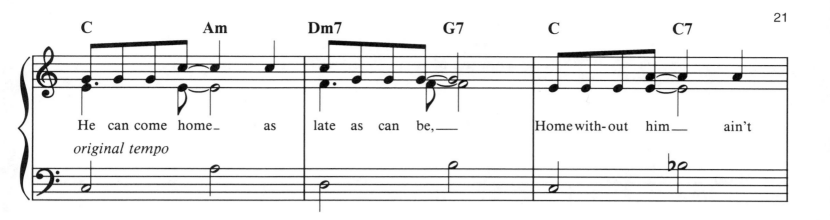

He can come home_ as late as can be,__ Home with-out him_ ain't

original tempo

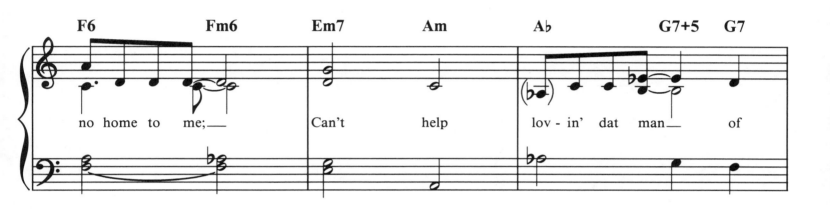

no home to me;__ Can't help lov - in' dat man_ of

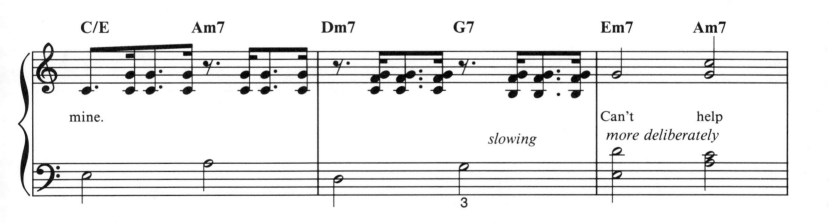

mine. *slowing* Can't help

more deliberately

3

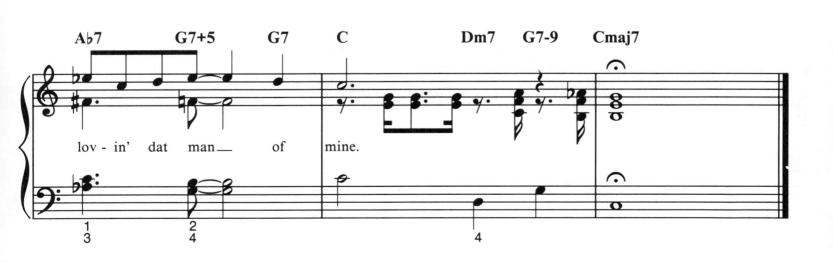

lov - in' dat man_ of mine.

1 2
3 4 4

CABARET
from the Musical CABARET

Words by FRED EBB
Music by JOHN KANDER

23

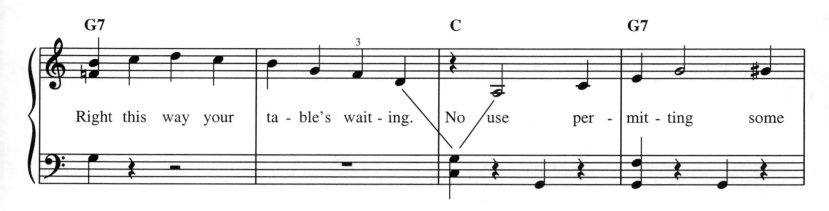

Right this way your ta - ble's wait - ing. No use per - mit - ting some

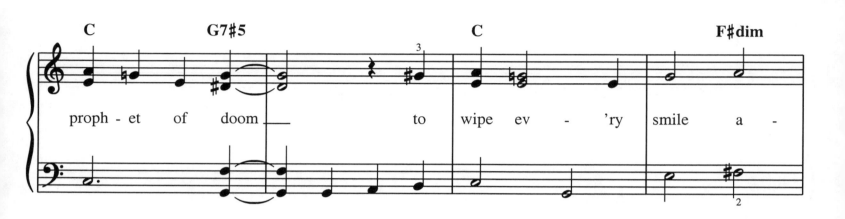

proph - et of doom to wipe ev - 'ry smile a -

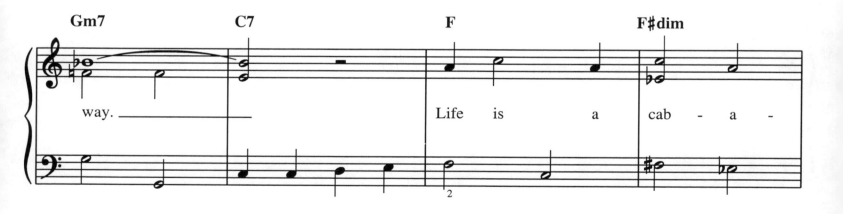

way. Life is a cab - a -

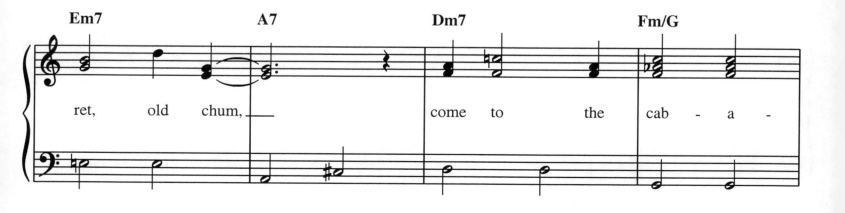

ret, old chum, come to the cab - a -

Slightly faster

ret!   I

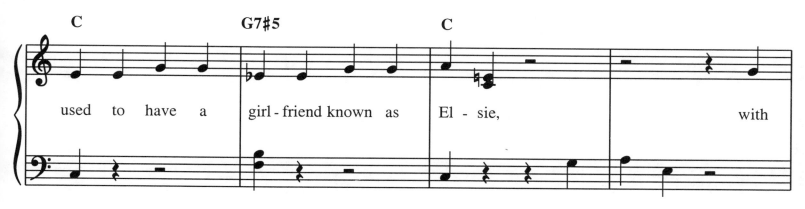

used to have a girl-friend known as El - sie,   with

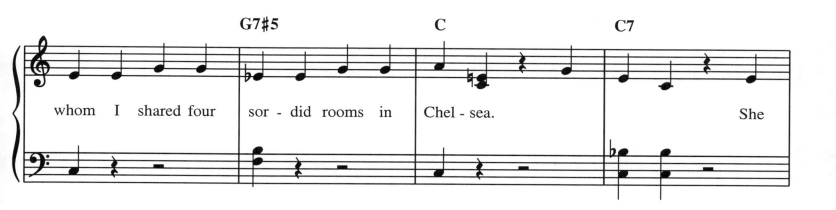

whom I shared four sor - did rooms in Chel - sea.   She

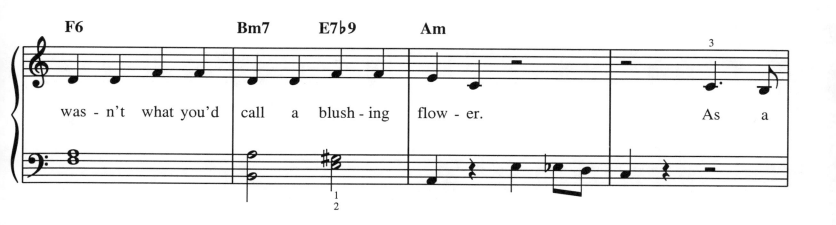

was - n't what you'd call a blush-ing flow - er.   As a

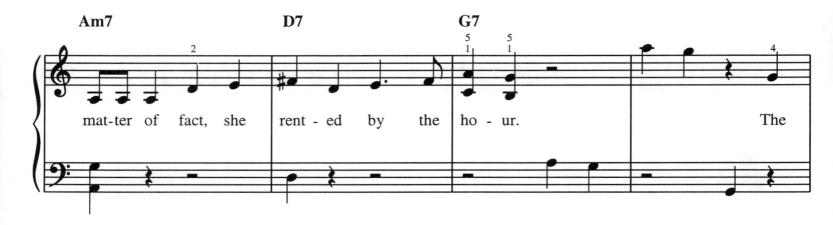

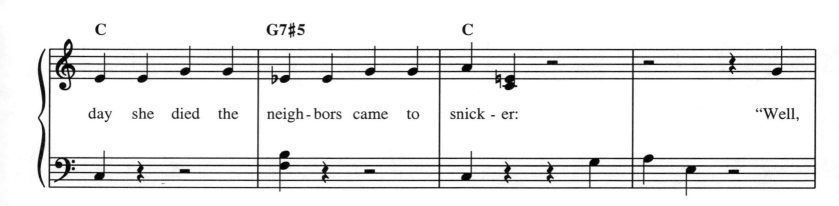

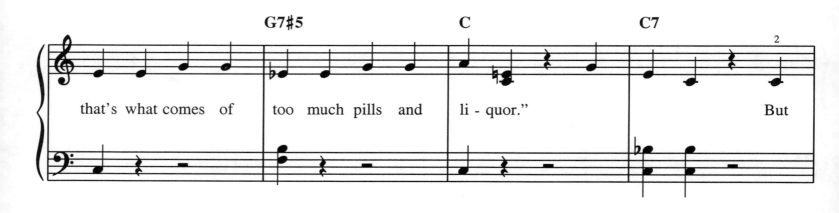

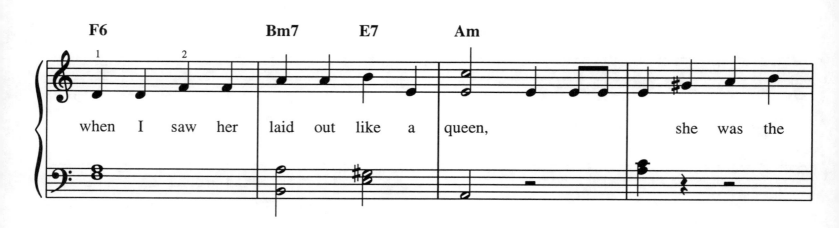

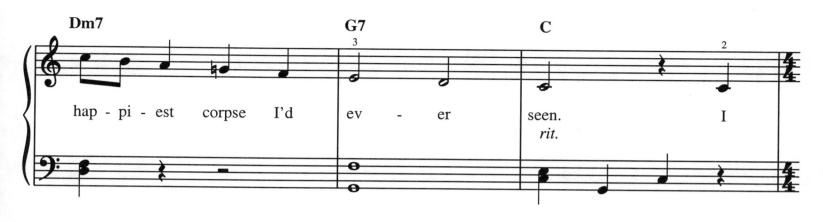

hap - pi - est corpse I'd ev - er seen. I

rit.

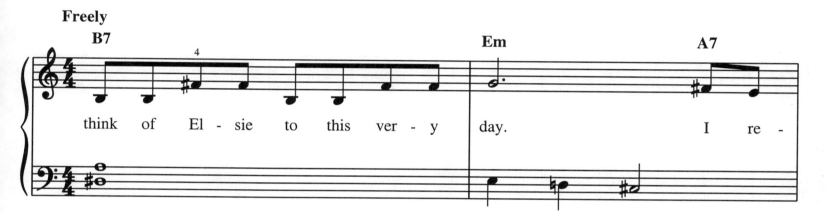

Freely

think of El - sie to this ver - y day. I re -

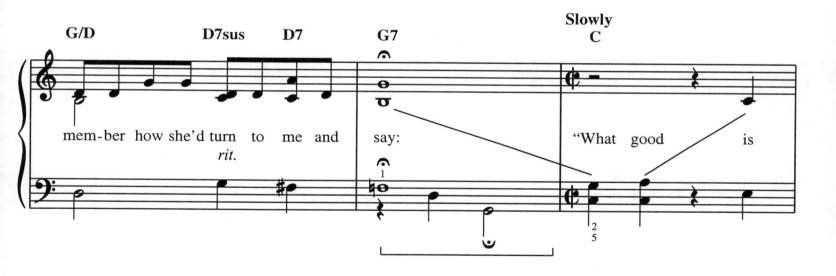

mem - ber how she'd turn to me and say: "What good is

rit. **Slowly**

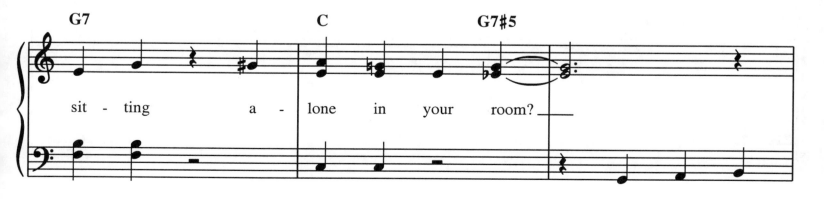

sit - ting a - lone in your room?___

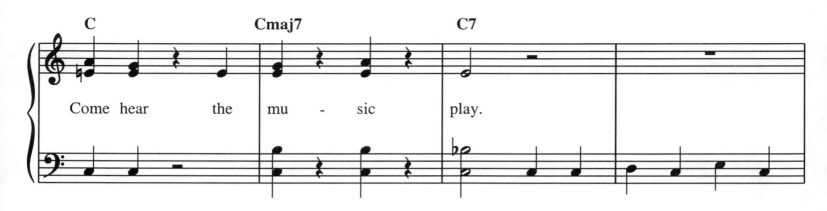

Come hear the mu - sic play.

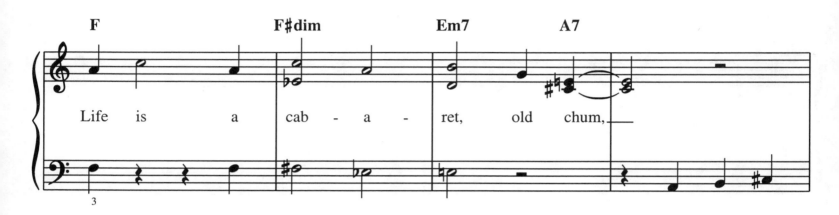

Life is a cab - a - ret, old chum, ___

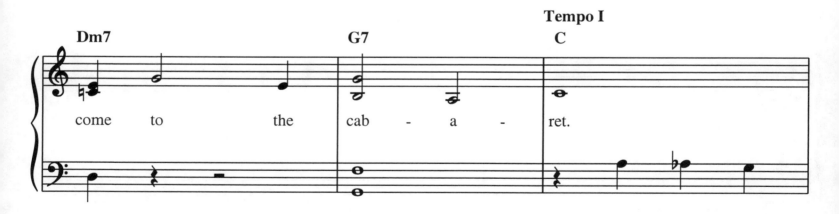

come to the cab - a - ret.

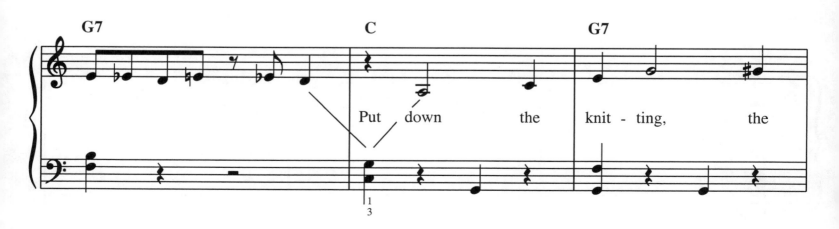

Put down the knit - ting, the

book and the broom. ___ Time for a hol - i -

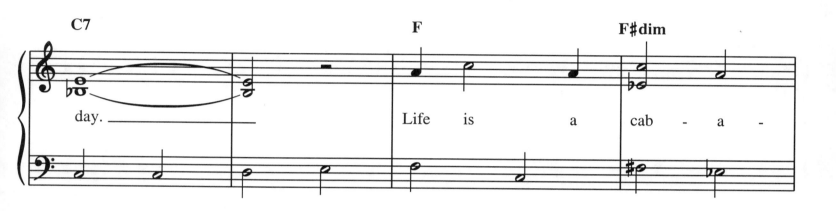

day. ___ Life is a cab - a -

ret, old chum, ___ come to the cab - a -

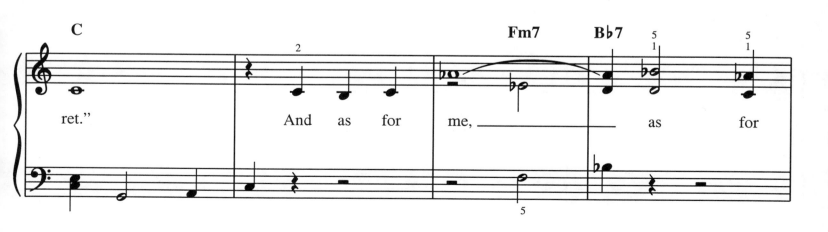

ret." And as for me, ___ as for

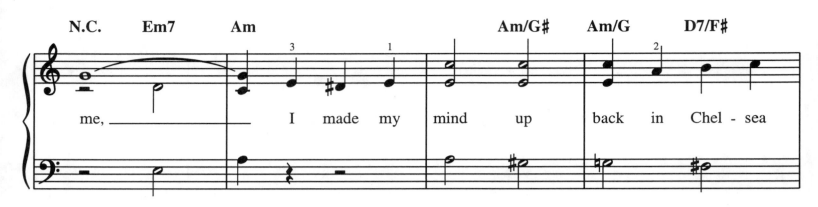

N.C.   **Em7**   **Am**   **Am/G♯**   **Am/G**   **D7/F♯**

me, _____   I made my mind up back in Chel - sea

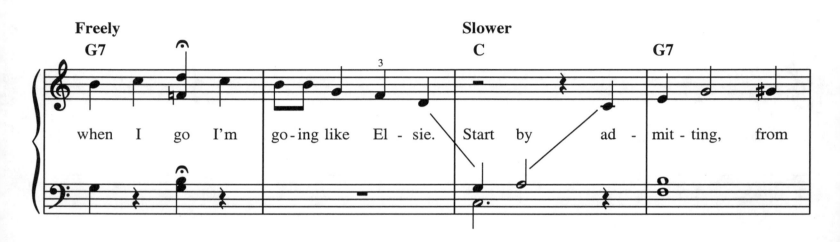

Freely   **Slower**
G7   **C**   **G7**

when I go I'm go-ing like El - sie. Start by ad - mit - ting, from

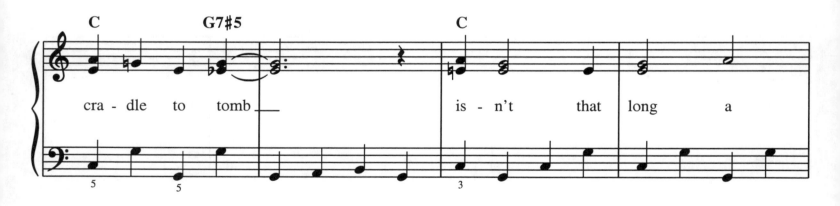

C   **G7♯5**   **C**

cra - dle to tomb ___   is - n't that long a

Tempo I
Gm7   **C7**   **F**   **F♯dim**

stay.   Life is a cab - a -

gradually faster

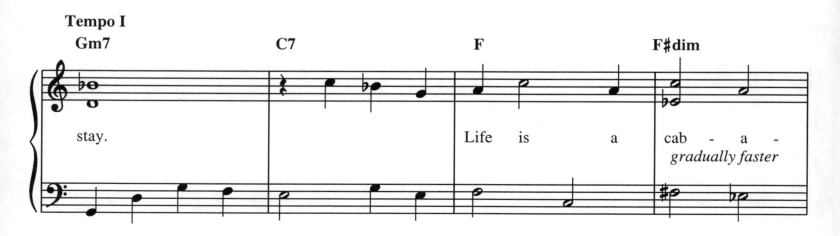

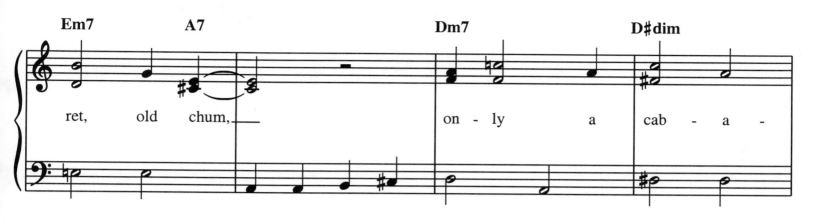

ret,　　old　chum,　　　　　　on - ly　a　cab - a -

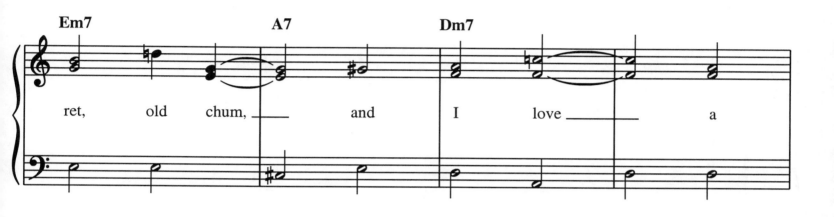

ret,　　old　chum,　　　　and　I　love　　　a

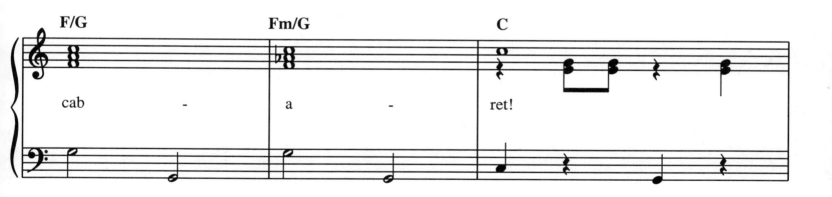

cab　-　a　-　ret!

CLIMB EV'RY MOUNTAIN
from THE SOUND OF MUSIC

Lyrics by OSCAR HAMMERSTEIN II
Music by RICHARD RODGERS

Majestically

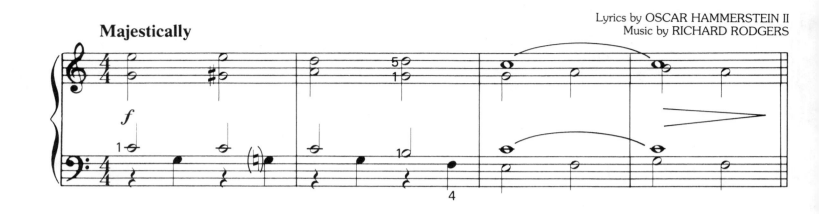

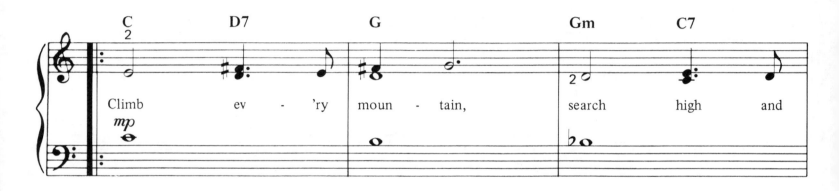

Climb ev - 'ry moun - tain, search high and

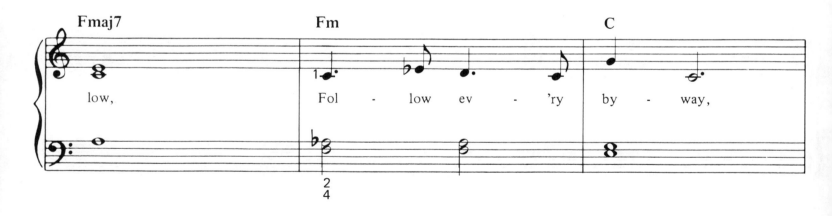

low, Fol - low ev - 'ry by - way,

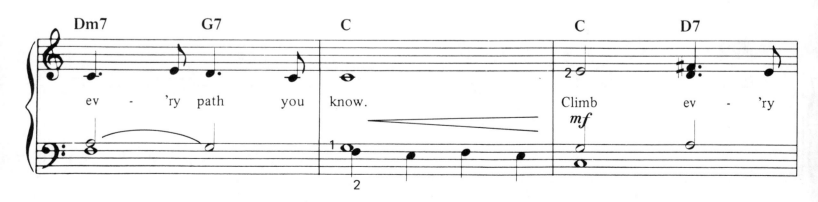

ev - 'ry path you know. Climb ev - 'ry

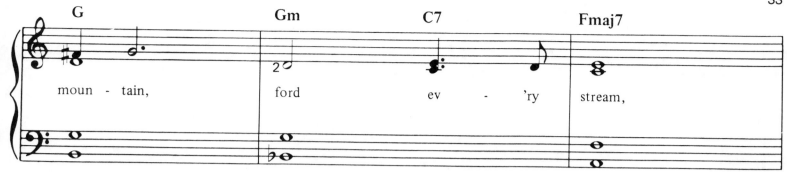

mountain, ford ev - 'ry stream,

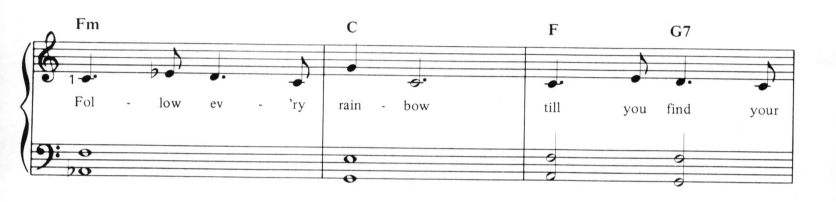

Fol - low ev - 'ry rain - bow till you find your

dream! A dream that will need all the love you can

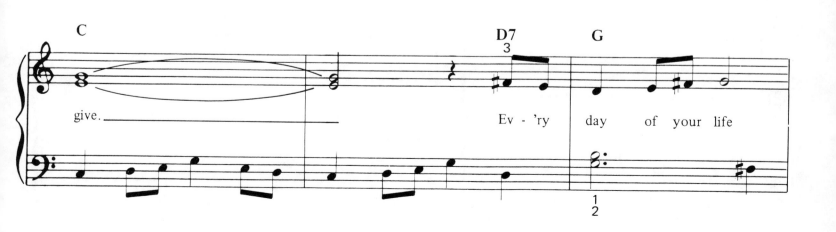

give._____ Ev - 'ry day of your life

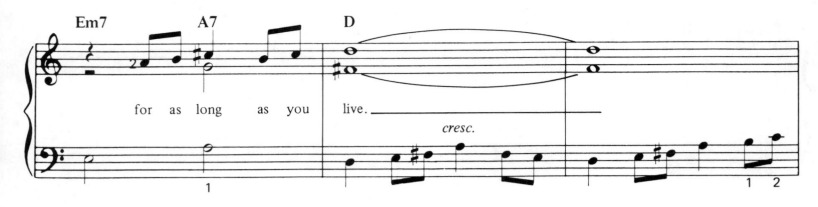

for as long as you live. _____

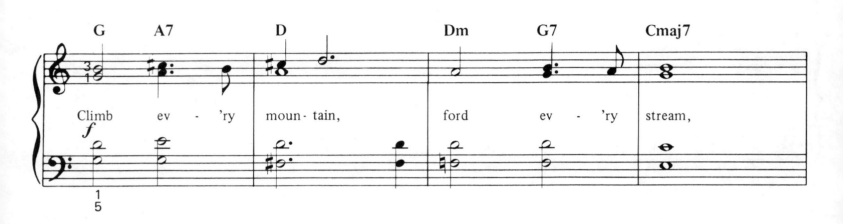

Climb ev - 'ry moun - tain, ford ev - 'ry stream,

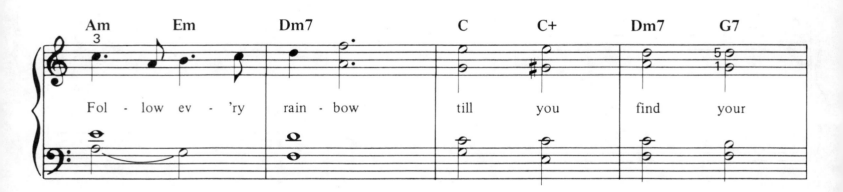

Fol - low ev - 'ry rain - bow till you find your

dream! _____ dream! _____

GETTING TO KNOW YOU

from THE KING AND I

Lyrics by OSCAR HAMMERSTEIN II
Music by RICHARD RODGERS

Moderately *(gracefully and not fast)*

DON'T CRY FOR ME ARGENTINA

from EVITA

Words by TIM RICE
Music by ANDREW LLOYD WEBBER

Moderate Tango tempo

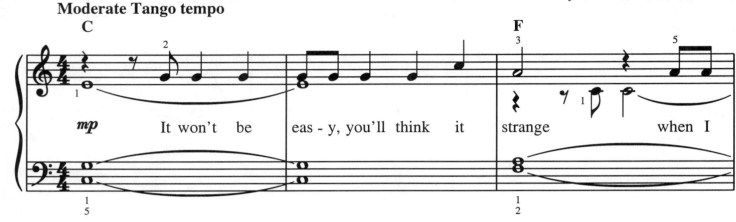

It won't be eas-y, you'll think it strange when I

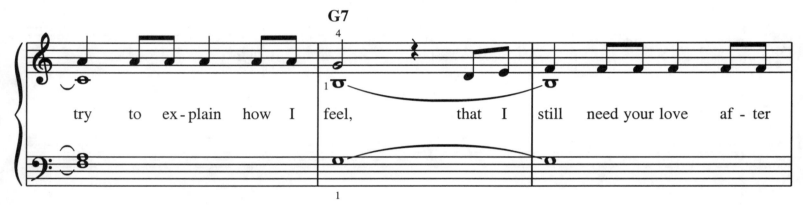

try to ex-plain how I feel, that I still need your love af-ter

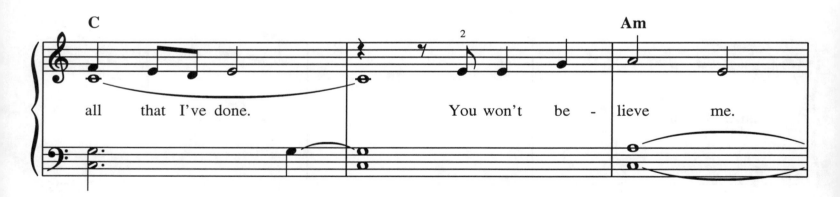

all that I've done. You won't be-lieve me.

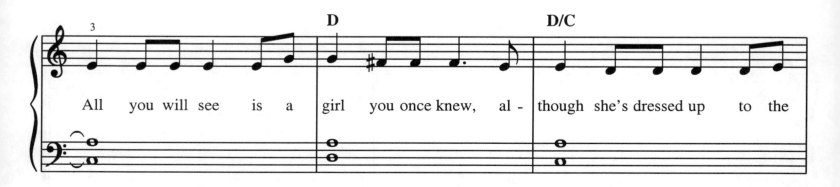

All you will see is a girl you once knew, al-though she's dressed up to the

nines   at   six - es   and   sev - ens   with   you.

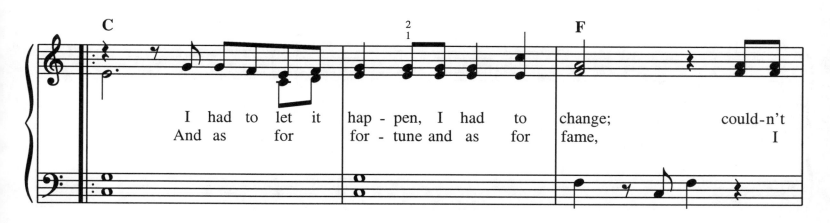

I   had   to   let   it   hap - pen,   I   had   to   change;   could-n't

And   as   for   for - tune and   as   for   fame,   I

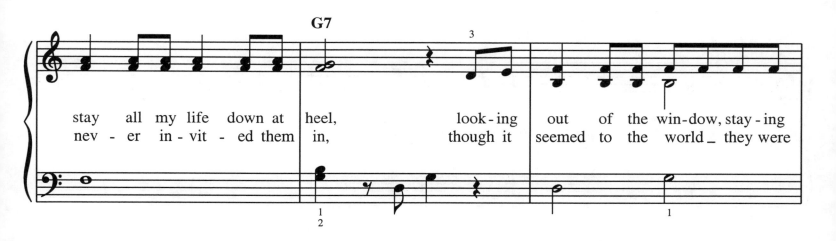

stay   all   my   life   down   at   heel,   look - ing   out   of   the   win - dow, stay - ing

nev - er   in - vit - ed them   in,   though   it   seemed   to   the   world _ they were

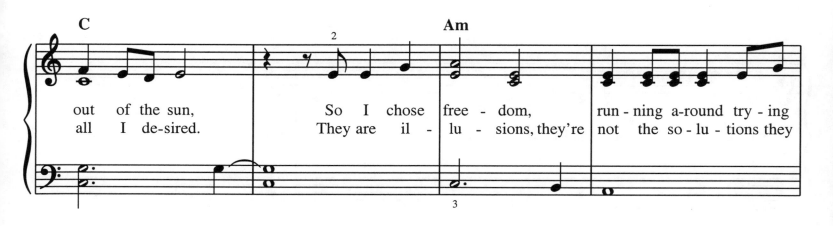

out   of   the   sun,   So   I   chose   free - dom,   run - ning a-round try - ing

all   I   de-sired.   They are   il - lu - sions, they're   not   the   so - lu - tions they

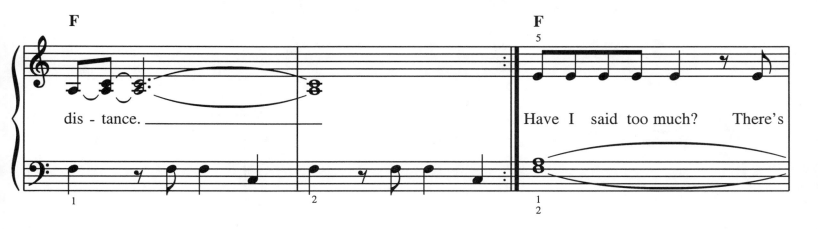

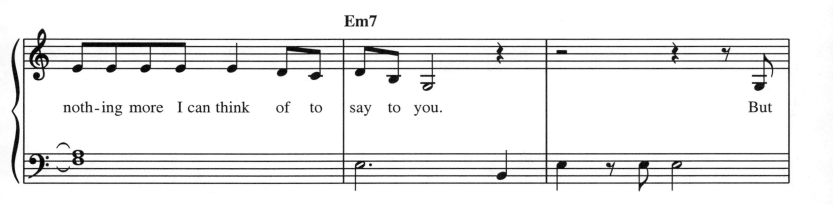

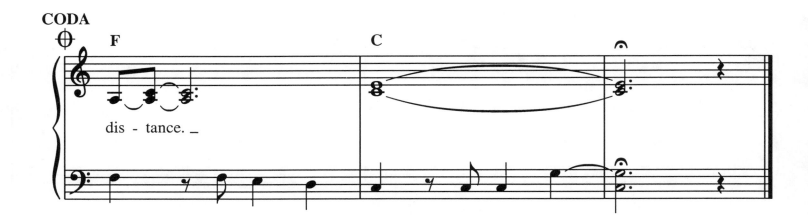

I DREAMED A DREAM
from LES MISÉRABLES

Lyrics by HERBERT KRETZMER
Original Text by ALAIN BOUBLIL & JEAN-MARC NATEL
Music by CLAUDE-MICHEL SCHÖNBERG

FANTINE:

I dreamed a dream in days gone by

when hope was high and life worth liv - ing.

I dreamed that love would nev - er die.

I dreamed that God would be for - giv - ing.

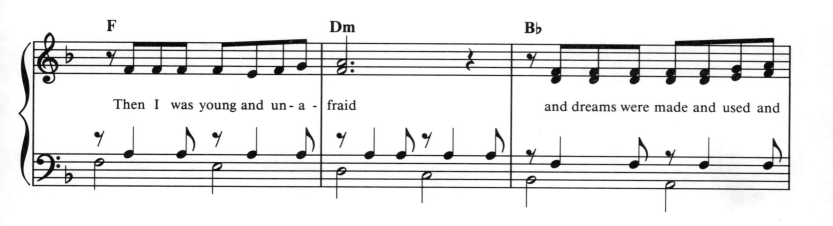

Then I was young and un-a-fraid

and dreams were made and used and

wast-ed.

There was no ran-som to be paid,

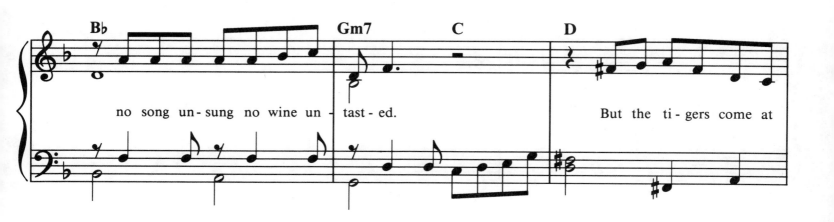

no song un-sung no wine un-tast-ed.

But the ti-gers come at

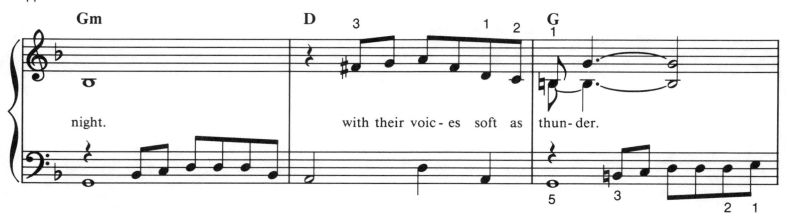

night.

with their voic-es soft as thun-der.

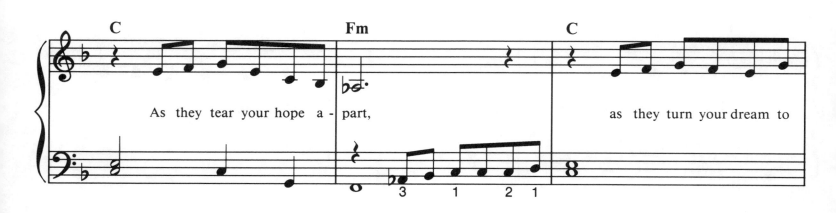

As they tear your hope a-part,

as they turn your dream to

shame.

rall.

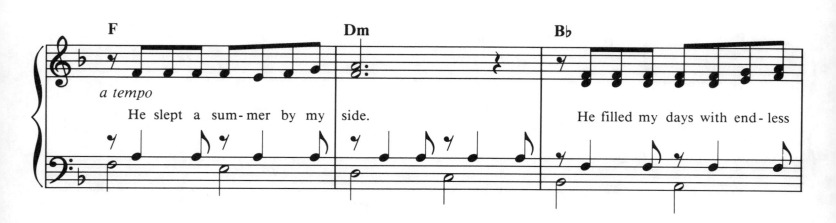

a tempo

He slept a sum-mer by my side.

He filled my days with end-less

IF I LOVED YOU

from CAROUSEL

Lyrics by OSCAR HAMMERSTEIN II
Music by RICHARD RODGERS

Cdim7   **C/E**   **C+**

loved you   words would-n't come in an eas - y way.

F6   **B7/F♯**   **C/G**   **Bm7♭5**   **E7**

'Round in   cir - cles I'd go.

Am   **F**   **B/F♯**   **E7**

Long - ing to tell you, but a - fraid and shy,

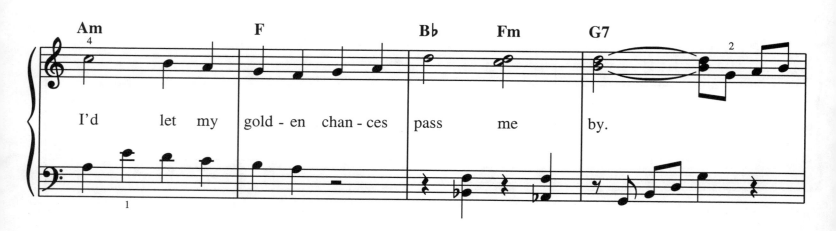

Am   **F**   **B♭**   **Fm**   **G7**

I'd let my gold - en chan - ces pass me by.

IF I WERE A RICH MAN

from the Musical FIDDLER ON THE ROOF

Words by SHELDON HARNICK
Music by JERRY BOCK

Proudly

If I were a rich man,   dai - dle, dee - dle, dai - dle,
Would - n't have to work hard,   dai - dle, dee - dle, dai - dle,

dig - guh, dig - guh, dee - dle, dai - dle,   dum.   All   day   long   I'd
dig - guh, dig - guh, dee - dle, dai - dle,   dum.   If   I   were   a

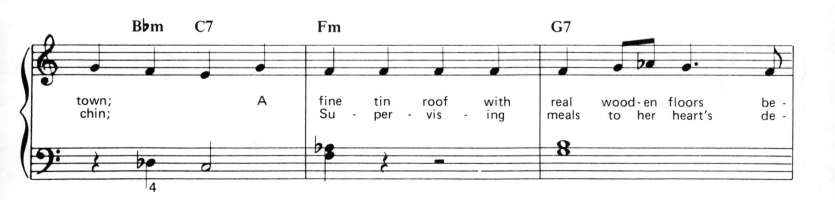

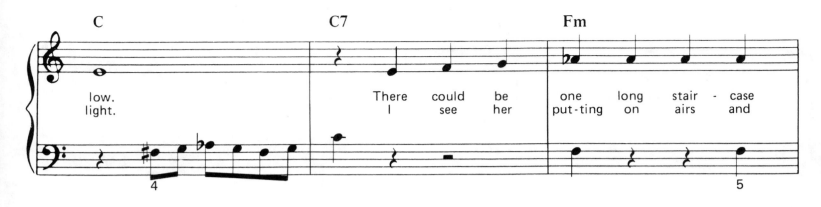

low. / light.

There could be / I could see her

one long stair - case / put-ting on airs and

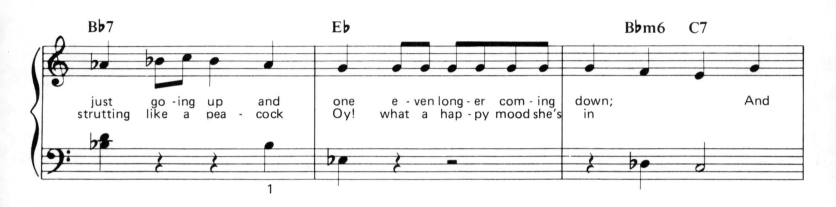

just go -ing up and / strutting like a pea - cock

one e -ven long -er com -ing / Oy! what a hap -py mood she's

down; / in

And

one more lead - ing / scream -ing at the

no - where just for / ser - vants day and

show. / night.

rit.

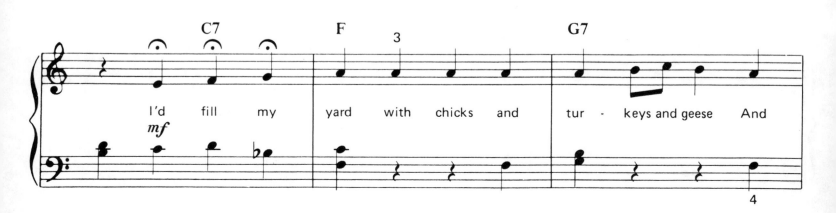

I'd fill my

yard with chicks and

tur - keys and geese And

mf

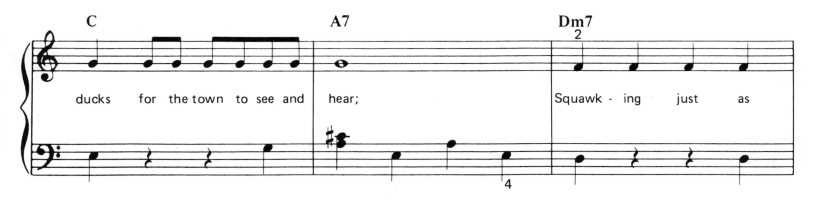

ducks   for the town to see and   hear;   Squawk - ing   just   as

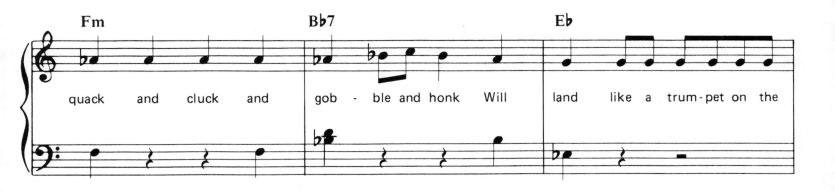

nois - i - ly   as   they   can.   And   each   loud

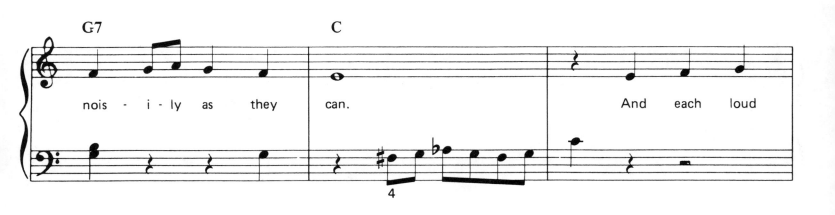

quack   and   cluck   and   gob - ble and honk   Will   land   like a   trum-pet on the

ear;   As   if   to   say   here   lives   a   weal - thy

54

D.S. al Coda
(with repeat)

CODA

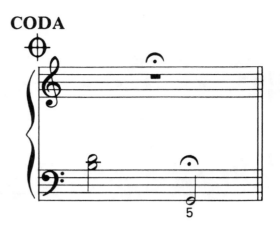

C

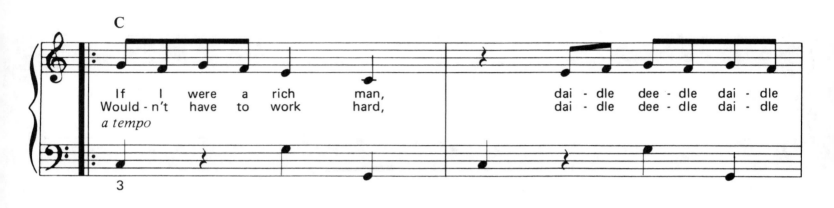

If   I   were   a   rich   man,   dai - dle   dee - dle   dai - dle
Would - n't   have   to   work   hard,   dai - dle   dee - dle   dai - dle
a tempo

3

dig - guh   dig - guh   dee - dle   dai - dle   dum.
dig - guh   dig - guh   dee - dle   dai - dle   dum.

1. **G7**   **Cm**   **F#dim**

All   day   long   I'd   bid - dy   bid - dy   bum,   if   I   were   a   wealth - y

Rubato

man. Lord, who made the li - on and the lamb,

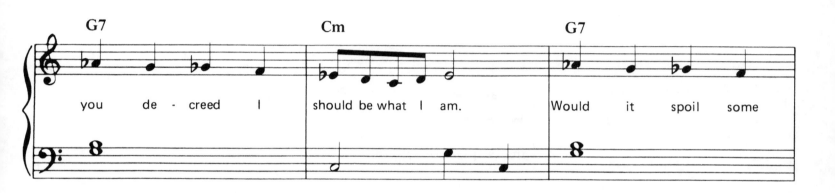

you de - creed I should be what I am. Would it spoil some

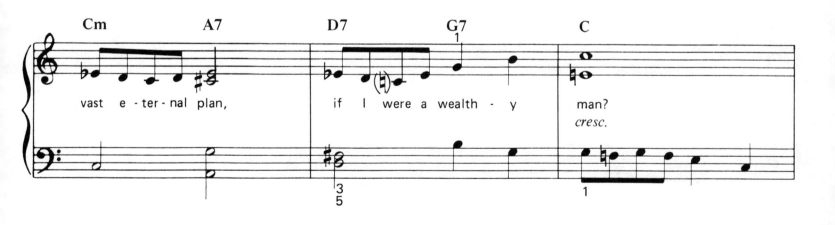

vast e - ter - nal plan, if I were a wealth - y man?
cresc.

f

THE LAST NIGHT OF THE WORLD
from MISS SAIGON

Music by CLAUDE-MICHEL SCHÖNBERG
Lyrics by RICHARD MALTBY Jr. & ALAIN BOUBLIL
Adapted From Original French Lyrics by ALAIN BOUBLIL

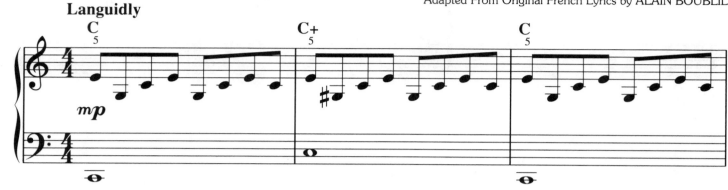

In a place that won't let us feel.

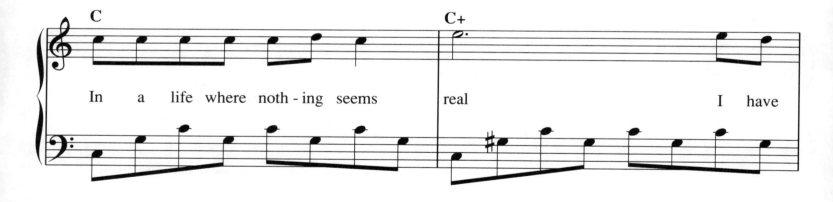

In a life where noth-ing seems real I have

found you, _ I have found you. _____

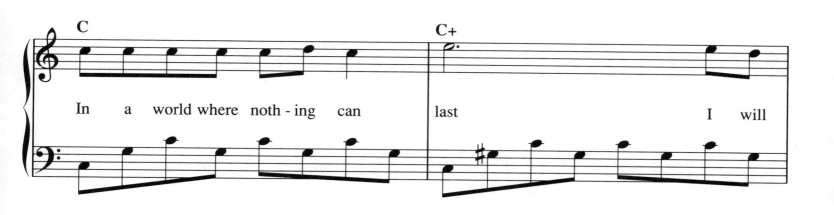

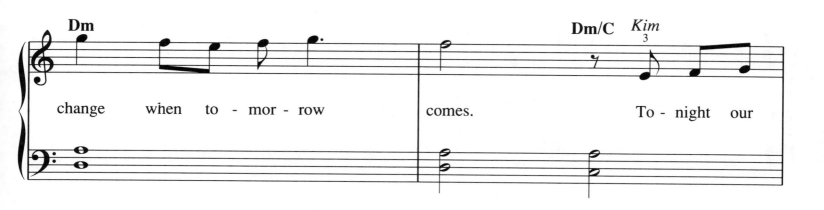

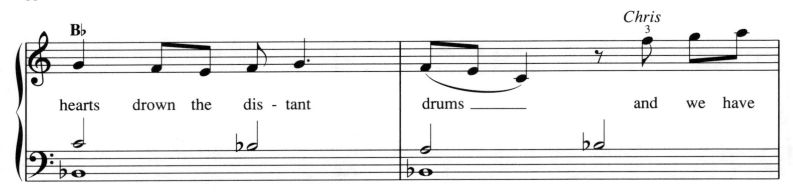

hearts drown the dis - tant drums _____ and we have

mu - sic al - right tear-ing the night. A song

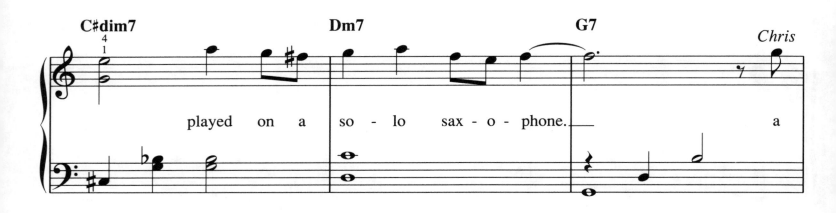

played on a so - lo sax-o - phone. _____ a

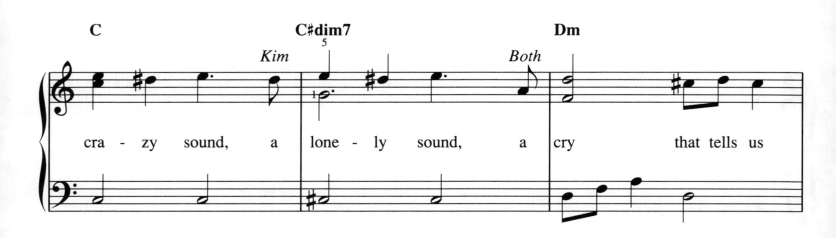

cra - zy sound, a lone - ly sound, a cry that tells us

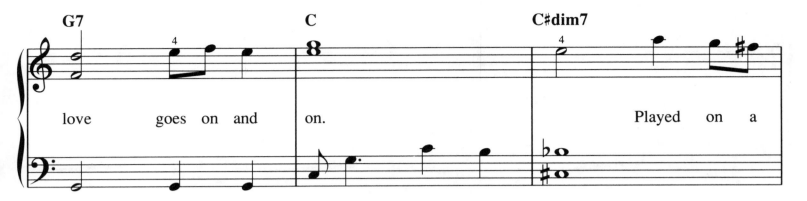

love   goes on and   on.   Played   on   a

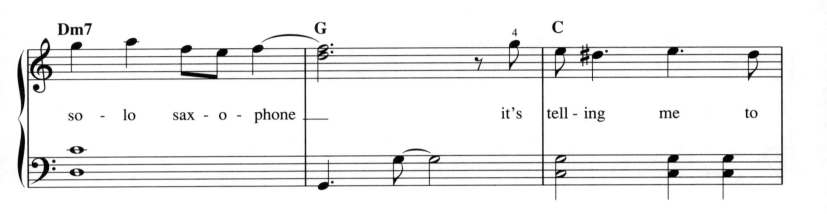

so - lo   sax - o - phone ___   it's   tell - ing   me   to

hold   you   tight   and   dance   like it's the last ___ night   of the

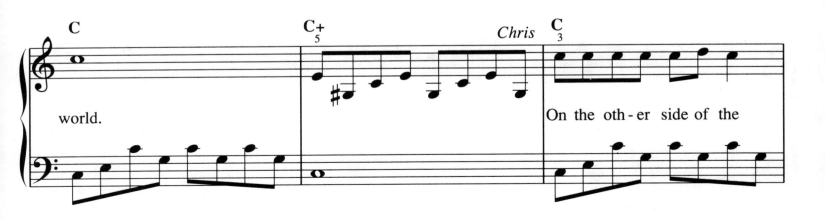

world.   *Chris*   On the oth - er side of the

earth | there's a place where life still has | worth. I will

take you._____ | I'll go with | you.____ You won't be -

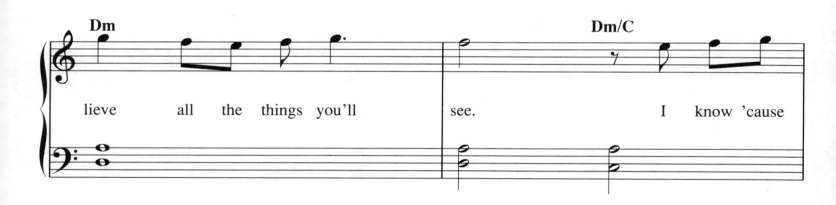

lieve all the things you'll | see. I know 'cause

you'll see them all with | me._____ If we're to - geth - er well then we'll

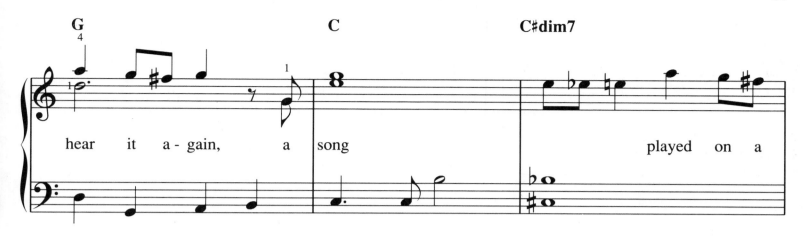

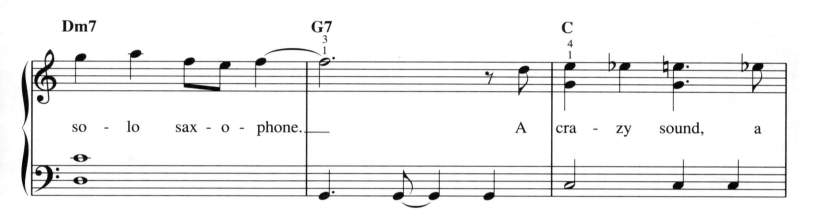

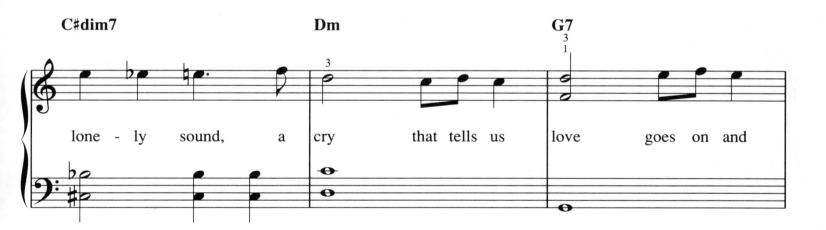

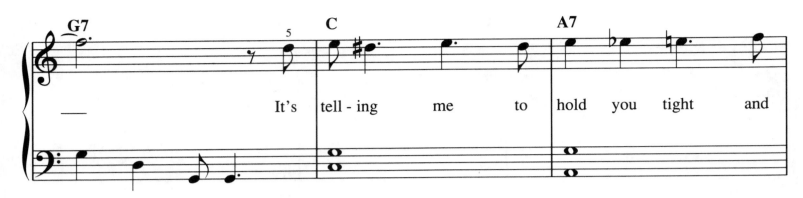

It's tell-ing me to hold you tight and

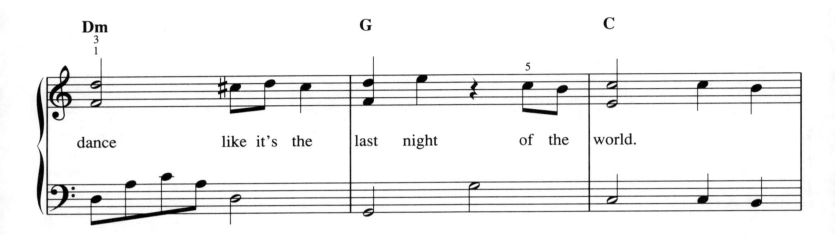

dance like it's the last night of the world.

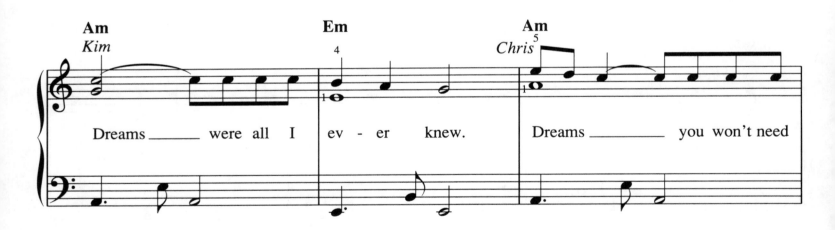

Dreams _____ were all I ev - er knew. Dreams _____ you won't need

when I'm through. An - y-where we may be,

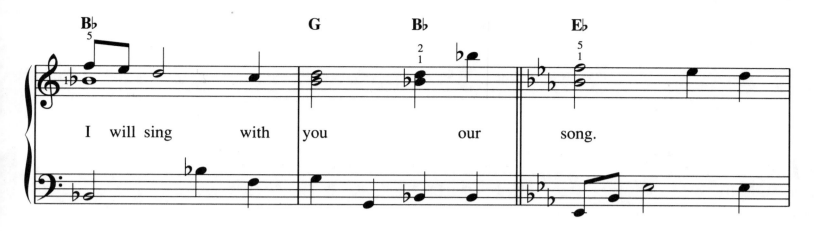

I will sing with you our song.

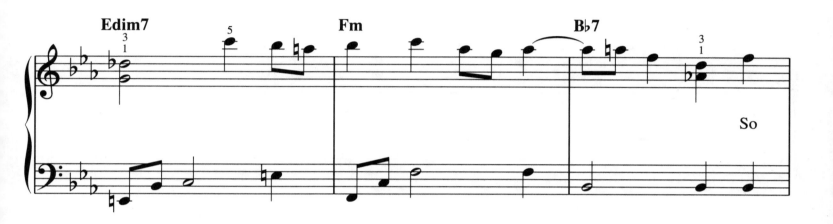

So

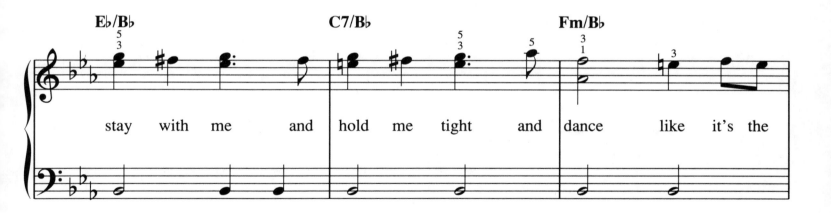

stay with me and hold me tight and dance like it's the

last night of the world. _____

ON MY OWN
from LES MISÉRABLES

Music by CLAUDE-MICHEL SCHÖNBERG

Lyrics by ALAIN BOUBLIL, HERBERT KRETZMER, JOHN CAIRD, TREVOR NUNN and JEAN-MARC NATEL

Slowly

With pedal

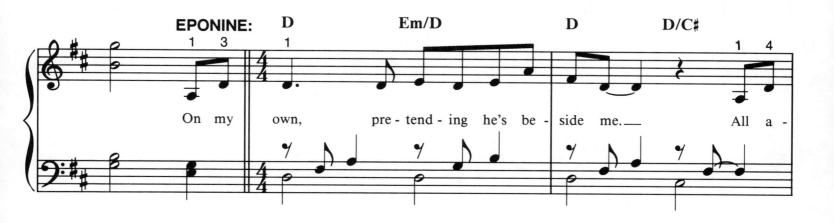

EPONINE:

On my own, pre-tend-ing he's be-side me. ___ All a-

lone I walk with him 'til morn-ing. With-out him I feel his arms a-

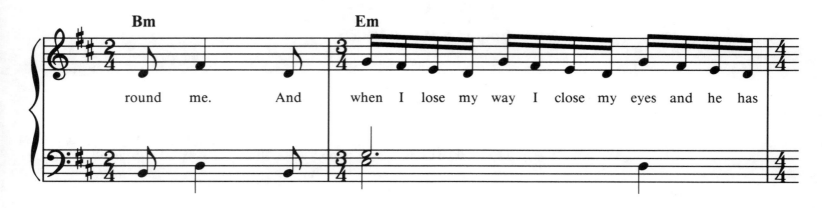

round me. And when I lose my way I close my eyes and he has

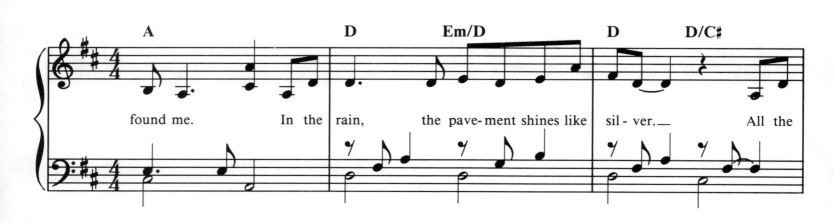

found me. In the rain, the pave-ment shines like sil - ver.__ All the

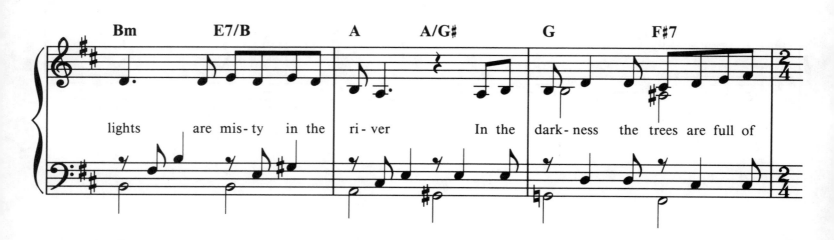

lights are mis-ty in the ri - ver In the dark-ness the trees are full of

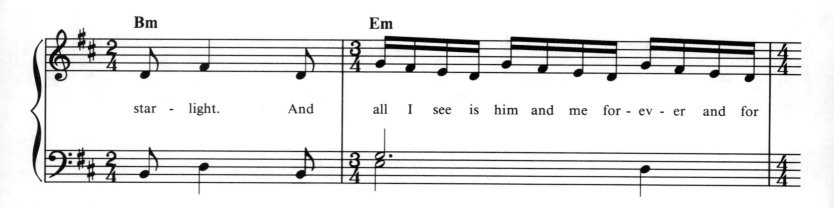

star - light. And all I see is him and me for - ev - er and for

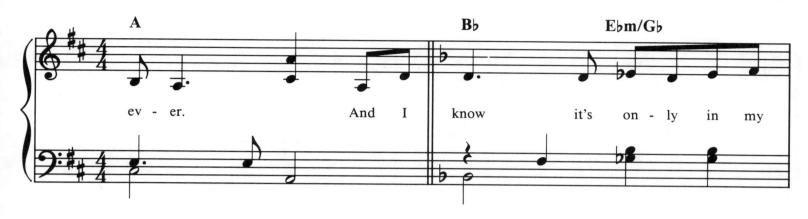

ev - er.   And I   know   it's on - ly in my

mind   that I'm talk - ing to my - self and not to him.   And al -

though   I know that he is blind,   Still I   say   there's a

way   for us.   I   love him,   but when the night is

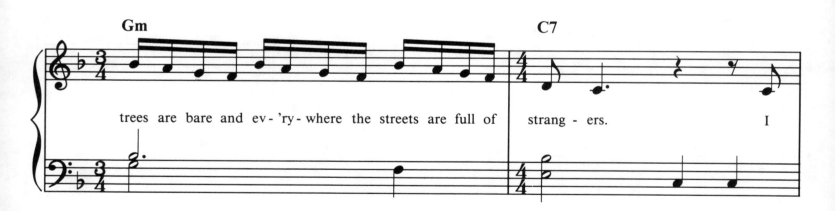

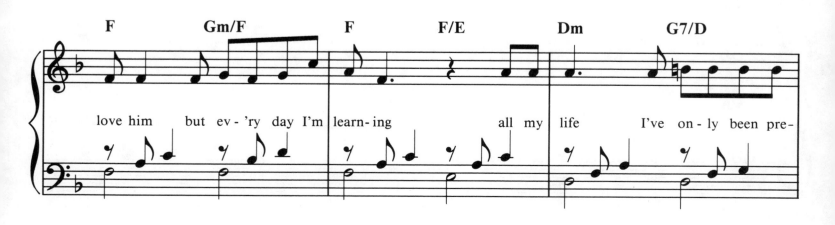

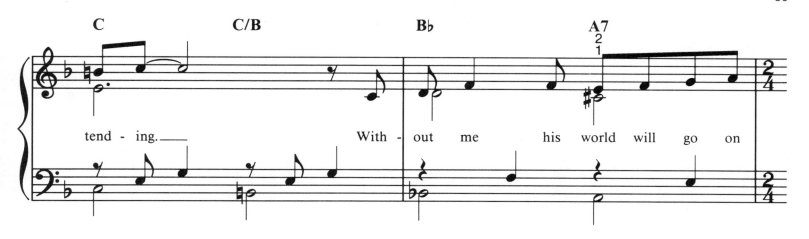

tend - ing.____ With - out me his world will go on

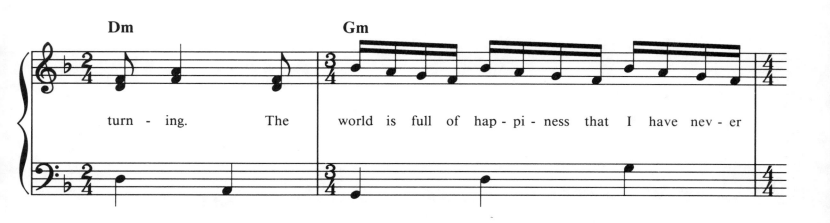

turn - ing. The world is full of hap - pi - ness that I have nev - er

known. I love him, I love him, I

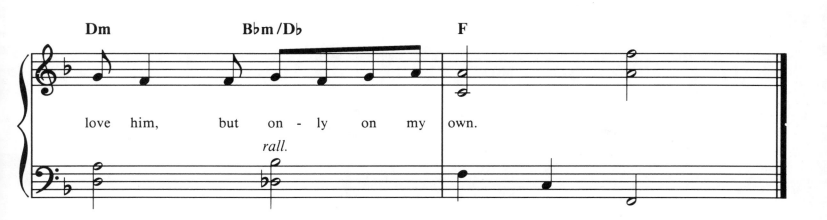

love him, but on - ly on my own.

rall.

MEMORY
from CATS

Music by ANDREW LLOYD WEBBER
Text by TREVOR NUNN after T.S. ELIOT

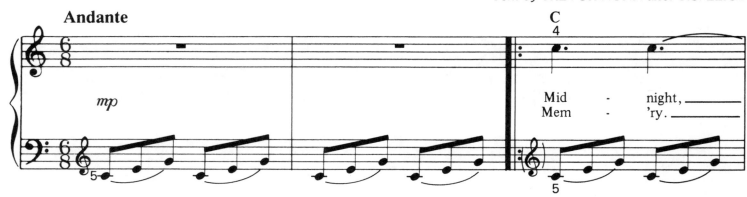

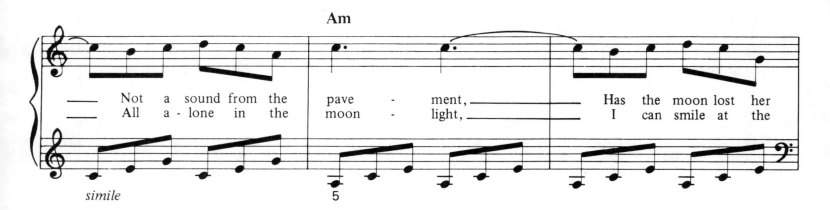

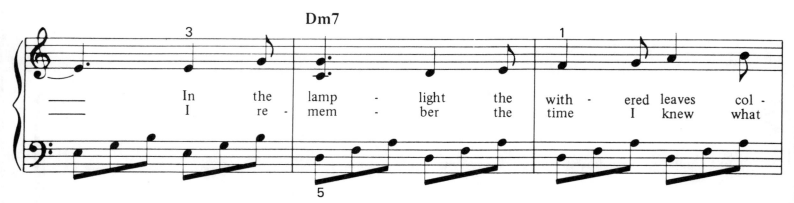

lect at my feet ____ And the wind ____
hap - pi - ness was ____ Let the (-)

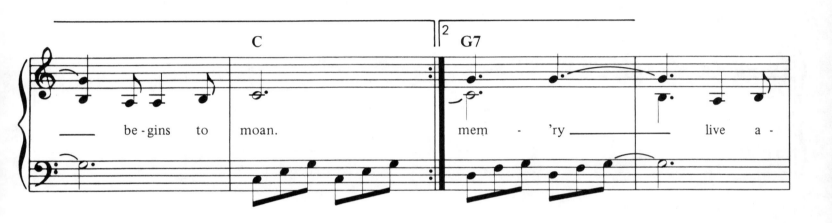

____ be - gins to moan. mem - 'ry ____ live a -

Faster, in two

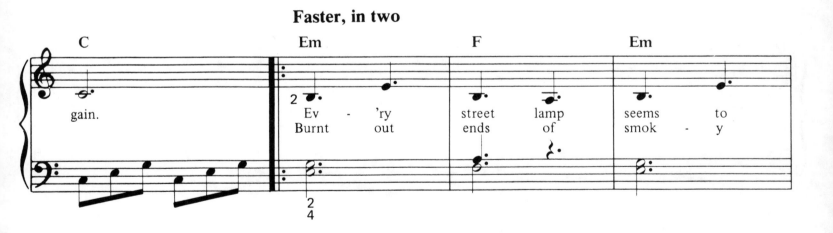

gain. Ev - 'ry street lamp seems to
Burnt out ends of smok - y

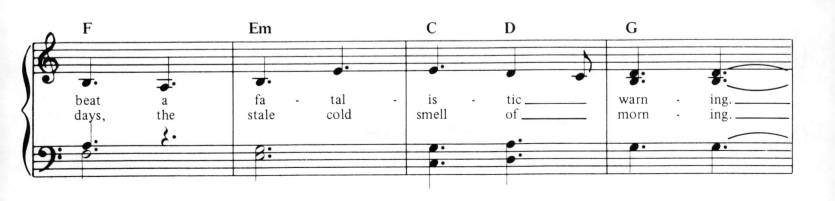

beat a fa - tal - is - tic ____ warn - ing. ____
days, the stale cold smell of ____ morn - ing. ____

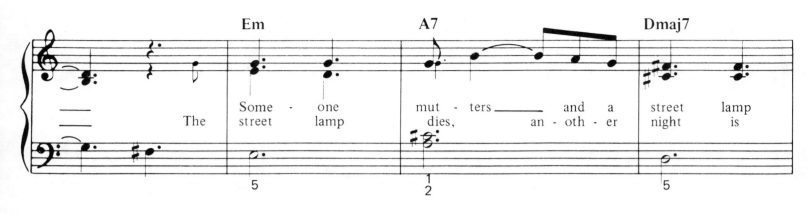

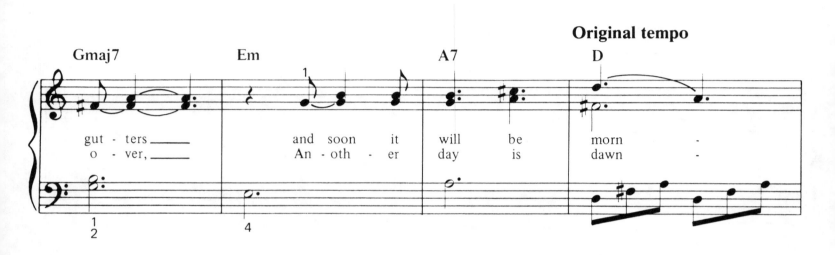

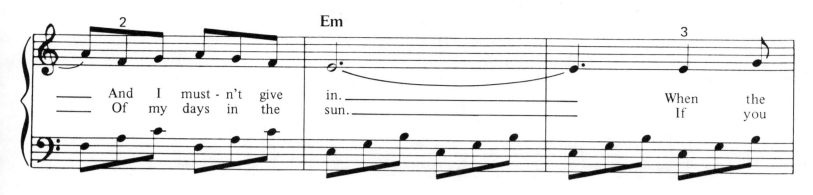

And I must-n't give in. When the
Of my days in the sun. If the you

dawn comes to - night will be a mem - o - ry too
touch me you'll un - der - stand what hap - pi - ness is,

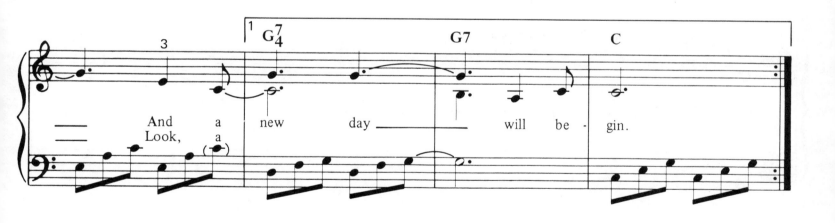

And a new day will be - gin.
Look, a a

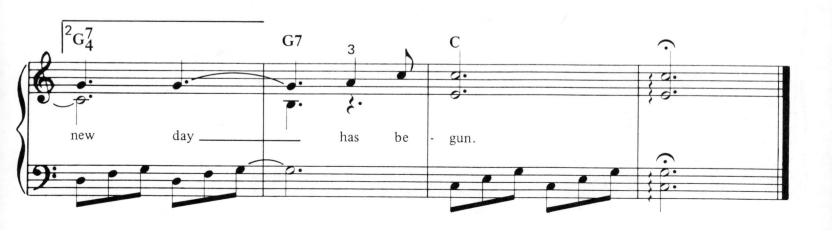

new day has be - gun.

A NEW LIFE
from JEKYLL & HYDE

Words by LESLIE BRICUSSE
Music by FRANK WILDHORN

Moderately slow, freely

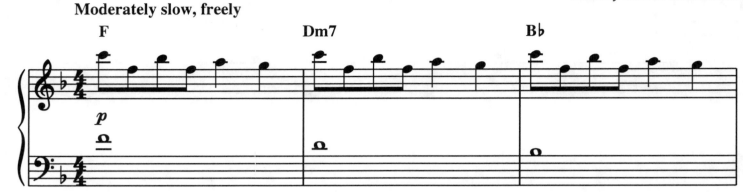

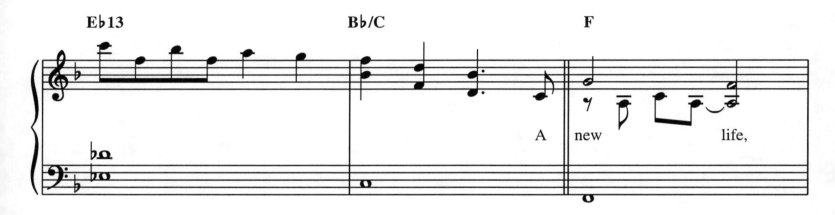

A new life,

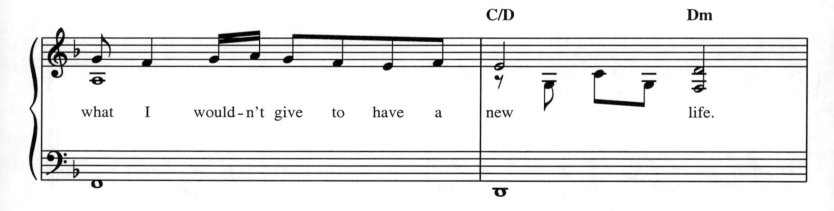

what I would-n't give to have a new life.

One thing I have learned as I go through life, through life,

noth-ing is for free a - long the way. A new start,

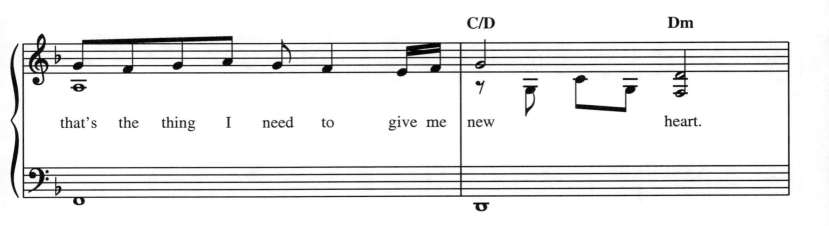

that's the thing I need to give me new heart.

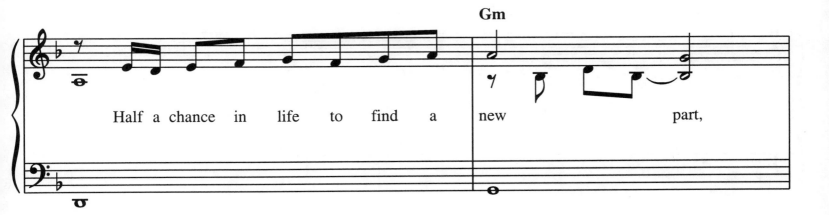

Half a chance in life to find a new part,

just a sim - ple role that I can play. A

me? A new dream,
I have one I know that ver - y

few dream.
I would like to see that o - ver - due dream,

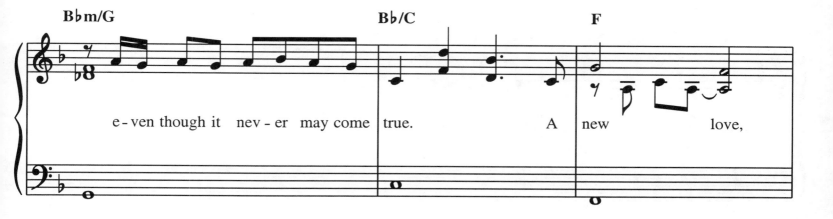

e - ven though it nev - er may come true.
A new love,

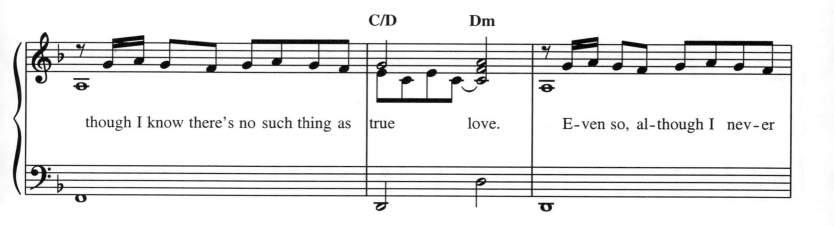

though I know there's no such thing as true love.
E - ven so, al - though I nev - er

knew love, still I feel that one dream is my due.

A new world, this one thing I want to ___ ask of

you, world. Once be-fore it's time to say a-dieu, world,

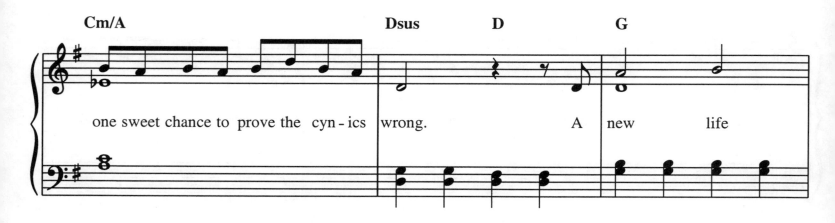

one sweet chance to prove the cyn-ics wrong. A new life

OH, WHAT A BEAUTIFUL MORNIN'
from OKLAHOMA!

Lyrics by OSCAR HAMMERSTEIN II
Music by RICHARD RODGERS

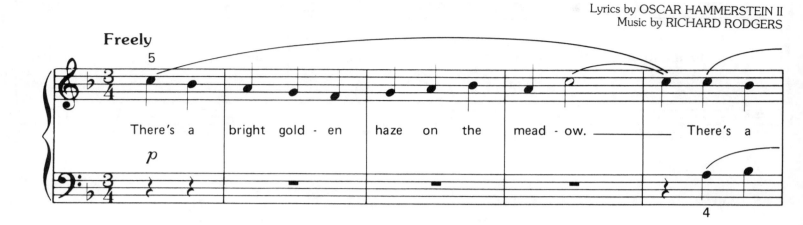

There's a bright gold - en haze on the mead - ow. There's a

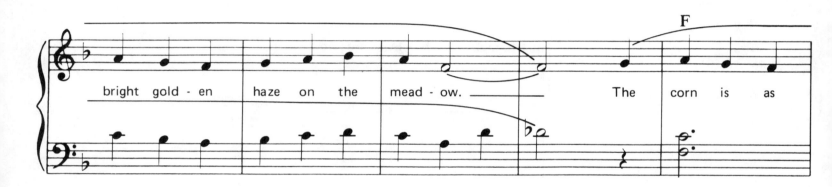

bright gold - en haze on the mead - ow. The corn is as

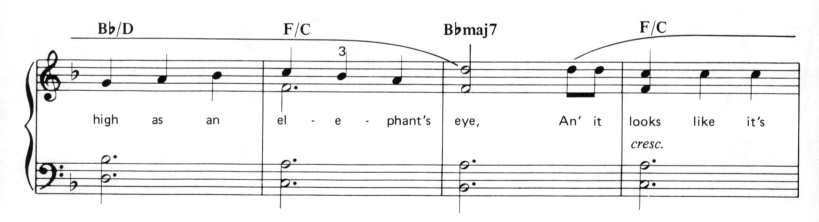

high as an el - e - phant's eye, An' it looks like it's

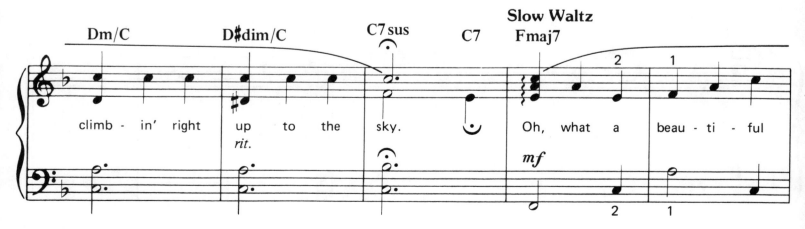

climb - in' right up to the sky. Oh, what a beau - ti - ful

morn - in', Oh, what a beau - ti - ful

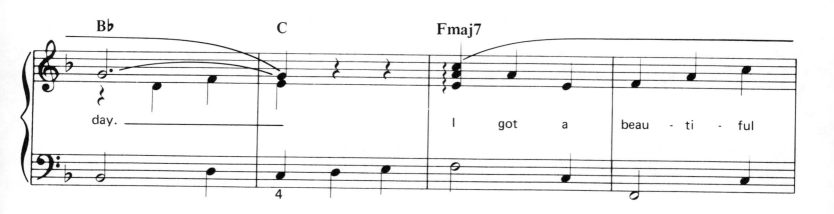

day. _____ I got a beau - ti - ful

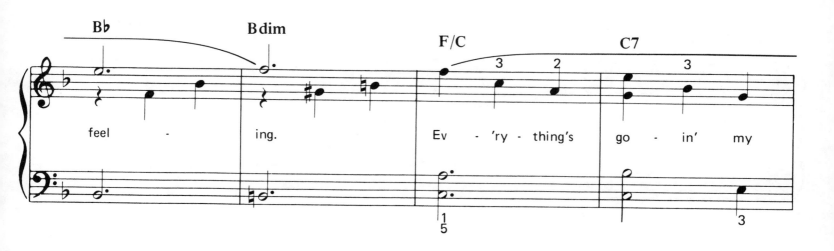

feel - ing. Ev - 'ry - thing's go - in' my

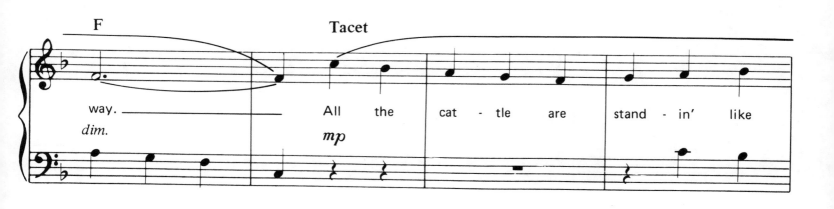

way. _____ All the cat - tle are stand - in' like

dim.   mp

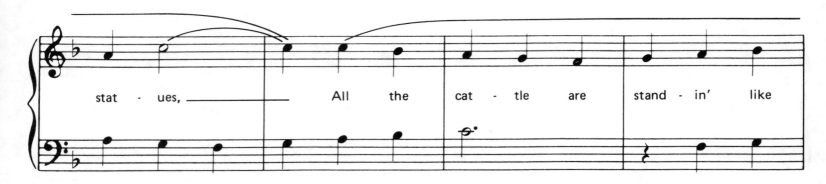

stat - ues, _____ All the cat - tle are stand - in' like

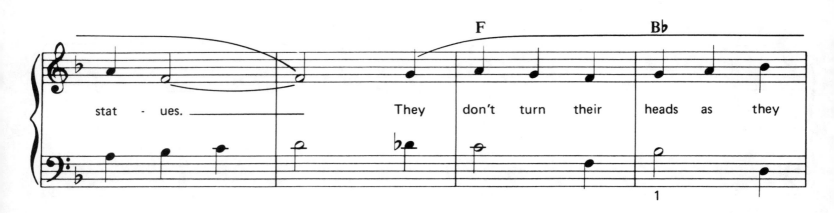

F   Bb

stat - ues. _____ They don't turn their heads as they

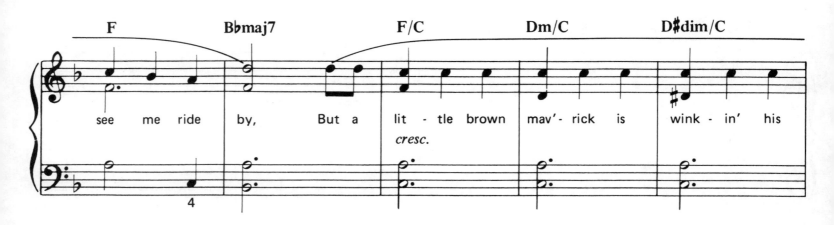

F   Bbmaj7   F/C   Dm/C   D#dim/C

see me ride by, But a lit - tle brown mav' - rick is wink - in' his
cresc.

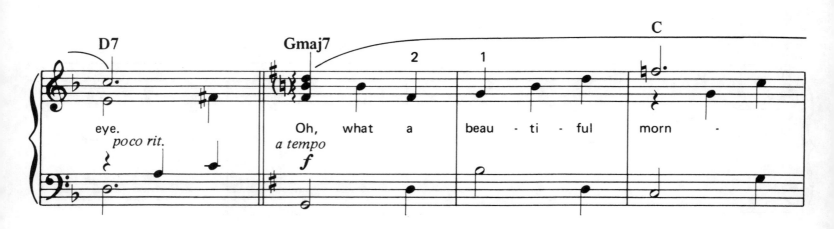

D7   Gmaj7   C

eye.   Oh, what a beau - ti - ful morn -
poco rit.   *a tempo*
f

in', Oh, what a beau - ti - ful day. _____

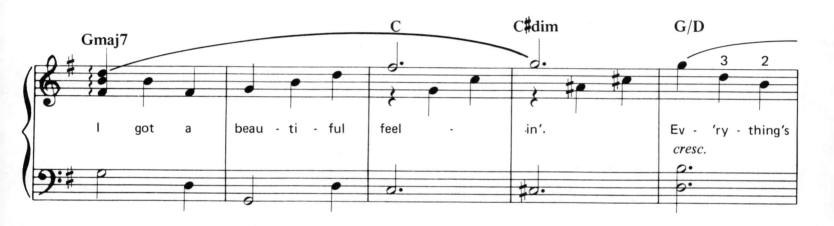

I got a beau - ti - ful feel - in'. Ev - 'ry - thing's
cresc.

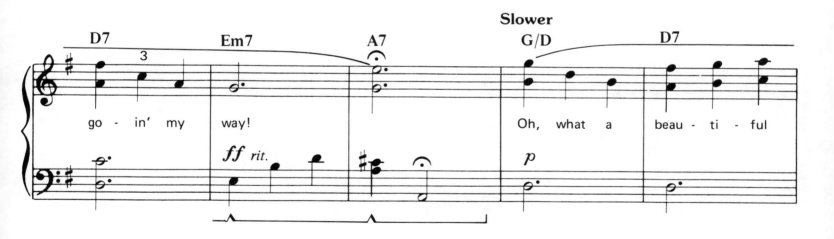

Slower

go - in' my way! Oh, what a beau - ti - ful
ff rit.   p

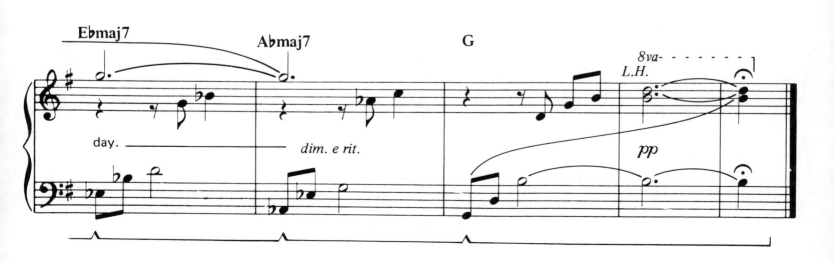

day. _____ G
dim. e rit.   pp

SEVENTY SIX TROMBONES

from THE MUSIC MAN

By MEREDITH WILLSON

band. Sev - en - ty horns____ of ev - 'ry shape and

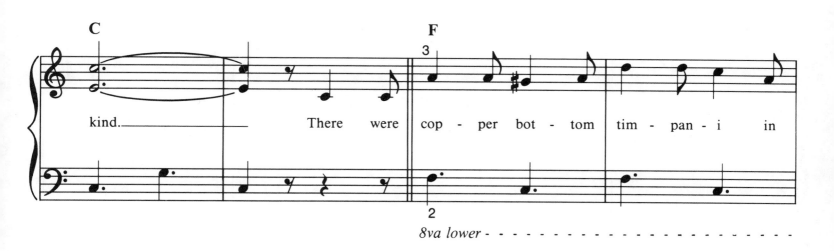

kind.____ There were cop - per bot - tom tim - pan - i in

8va lower -

horse pla - toons____ Thun - der - ing, thun - der - ing

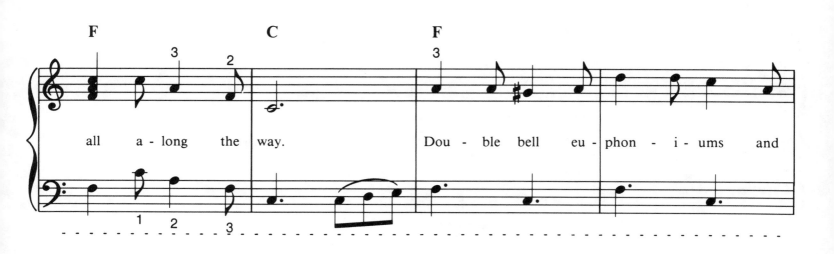

all a - long the way. Dou - ble bell eu - phon - i - ums and

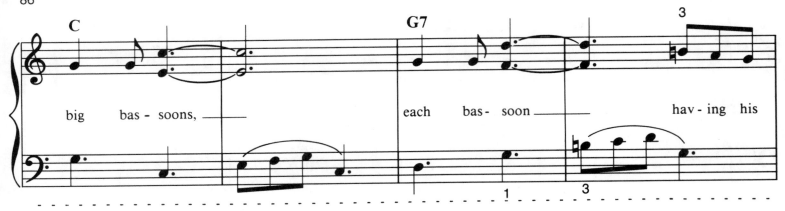

big bas - soons, _____ each bas - soon _____ hav - ing his

big fat say. There were fif - ty mount - ed can - on in the

bat - ter - y. _____ Thun - der - ing, thun - der - ing,

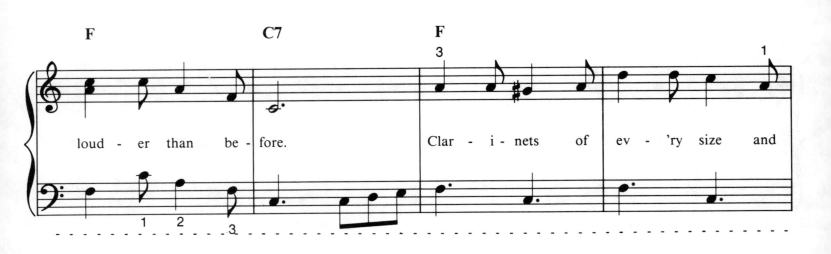

loud - er than be - fore. Clar - i - nets of ev - 'ry size and

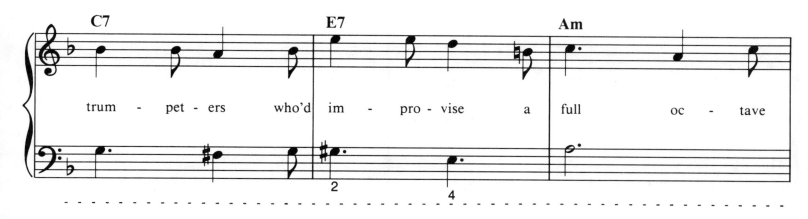

trum - pet - ers who'd im - pro - vise a full oc - tave

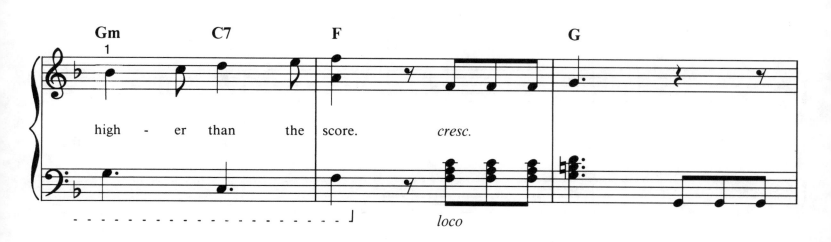

high - er than the score. *cresc.* *loco*

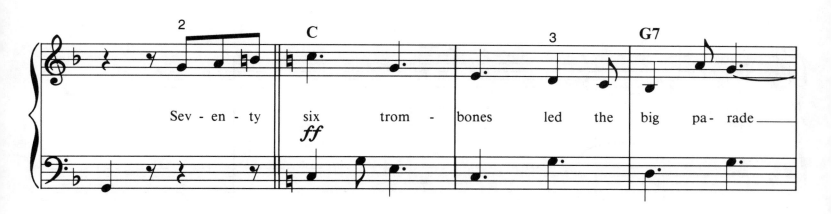

Sev - en - ty six trom - bones led the big pa - rade

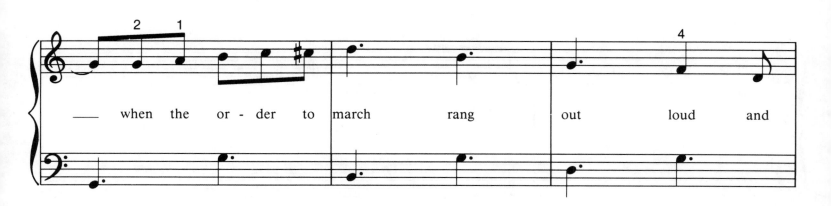

___ when the or - der to march rang out loud and

clear. _____ Start - ing off with a big bang bong on a

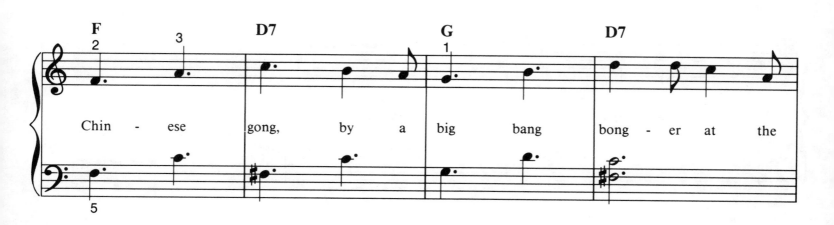

Chin - ese gong, by a big bang bong - er at the

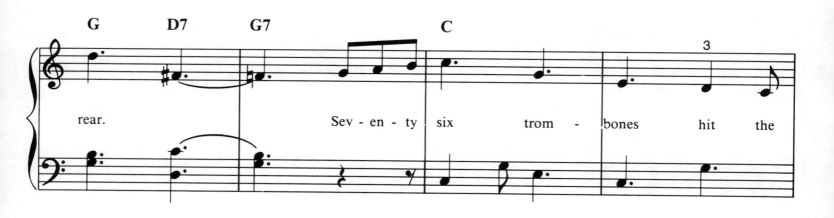

rear. Sev - en - ty six trom - bones hit the

coun - ter - point _____ while a hun - dred and ten cor -

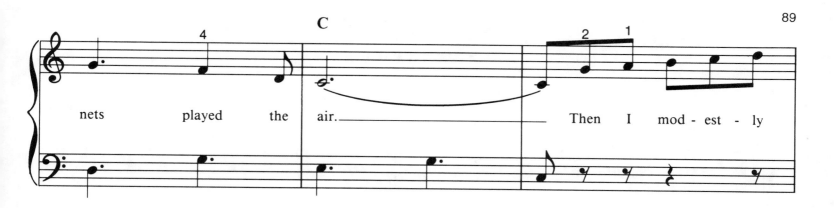

nets played the air._____ Then I mod-est-ly

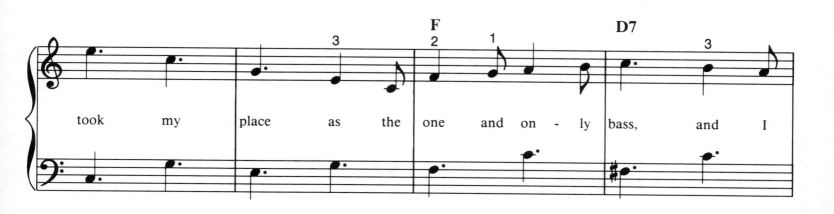

took my place as the one and on-ly bass, and I

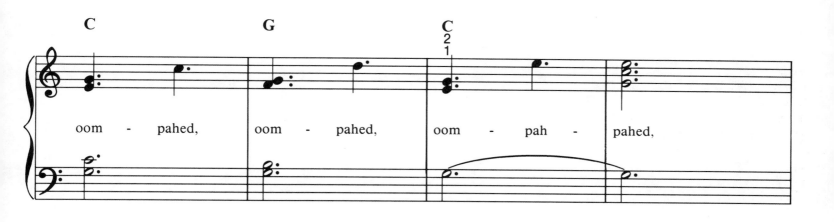

oom - pahed, oom - pahed, oom - pah - pahed,

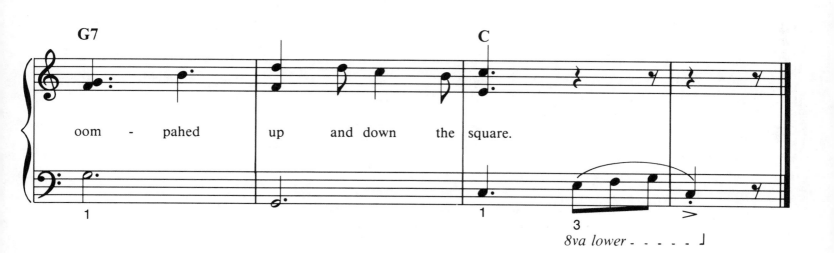

oom - pahed up and down the square.

8va lower - - - - -

SOME ENCHANTED EVENING

from SOUTH PACIFIC

Lyrics by OSCAR HAMMERSTEIN II
Music by RICHARD RODGERS

Some en-chant-ed eve - ning
Some en-chant-ed eve - ning

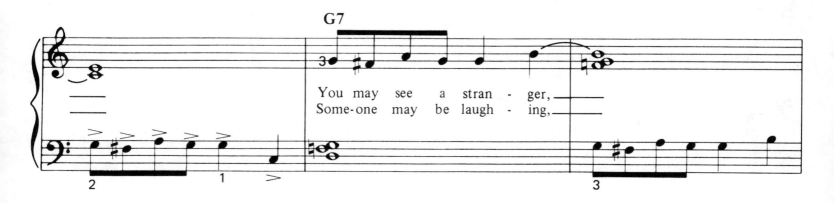

You may see a stran - ger,
Some-one may be laugh - ing,

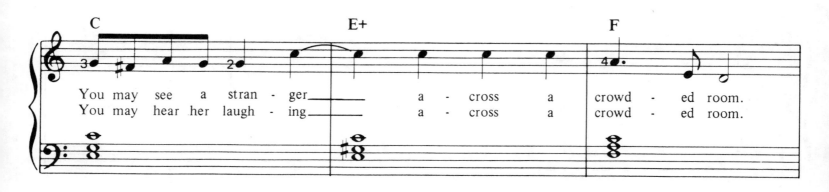

You may see a stran - ger a - cross a crowd - ed room.
You may hear her laugh - ing a - cross a crowd - ed room.

And some-how you know, you know e - ven
And night af - ter night, as strange as it

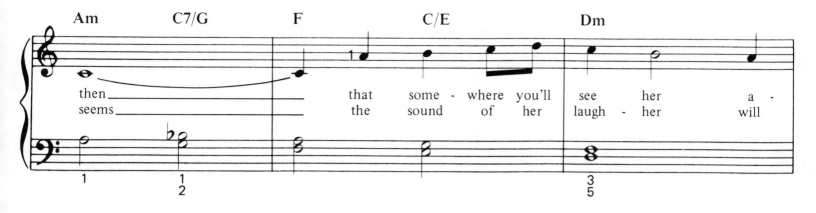

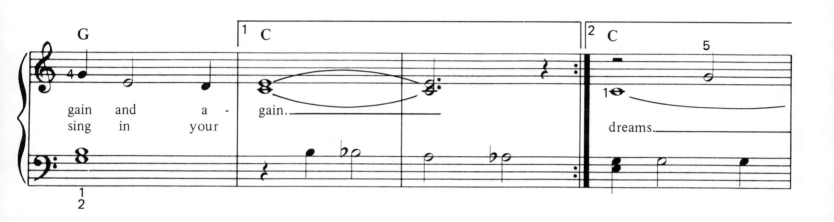

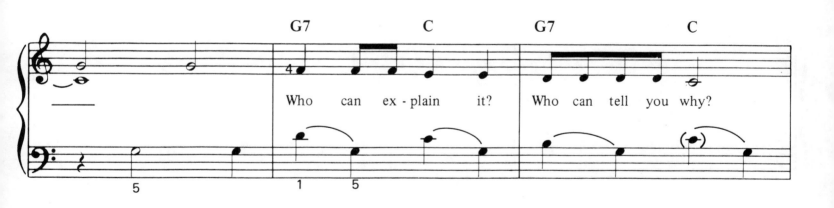

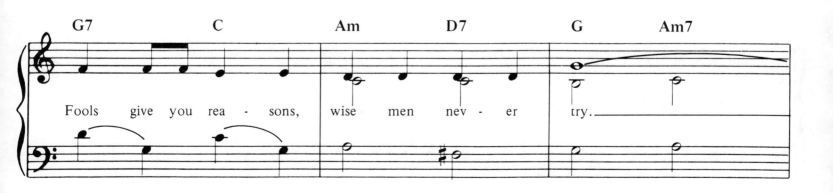

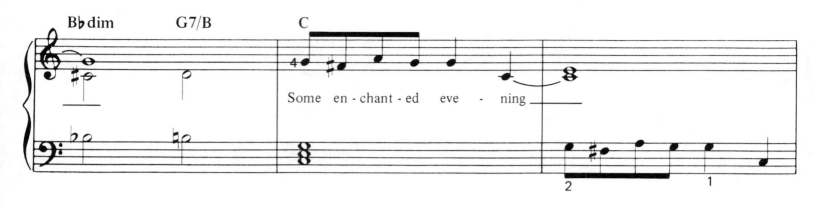

Some en-chant-ed eve - ning

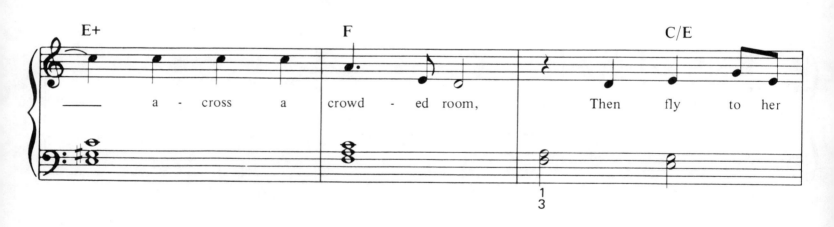

when you find your true love,⎯⎯ when you feel her call you⎯

⎯ a - cross a crowd - ed room, Then fly to her

side⎯⎯⎯ and make her your own⎯⎯

or all through your life you may dream all a-

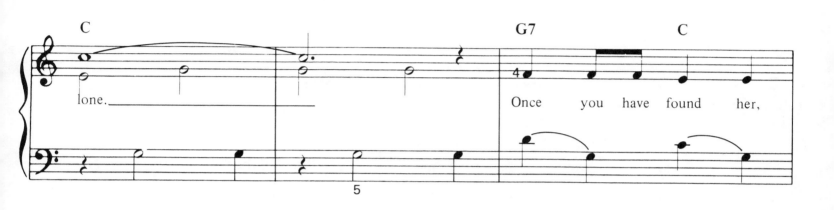

lone. Once you have found her,

nev - er let her go. Once you have found her nev - er

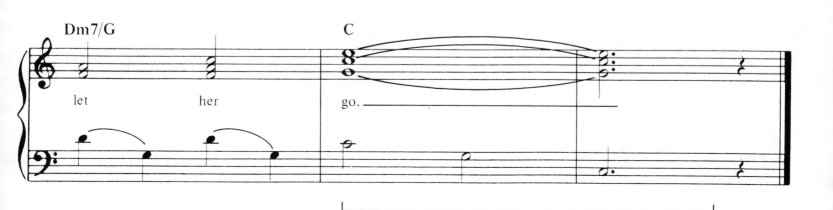

let her go.

STAYIN' ALIVE
from SATURDAY NIGHT FEVER

Words and Music by BARRY GIBB,
MAURICE GIBB and ROBIN GIBB

Some-bod - y help me._____ Some-bod - y help_ me yeah._

Em
Life go-in' no - where._

Some-bod - y help_ me yeah._ Stay-in' a-live.

Em

WITH ONE LOOK
from SUNSET BOULEVARD

Music by ANDREW LLOYD WEBBER
Lyrics by DON BLACK and CHRISTOPHER HAMPTON,
with contributions by AMY POWERS

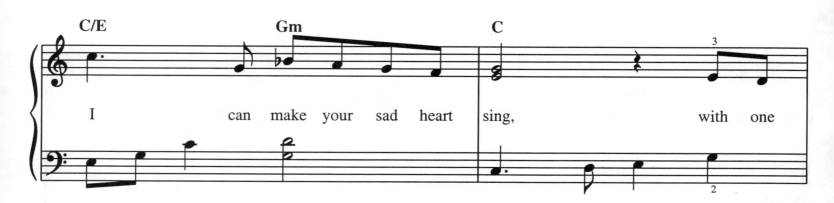

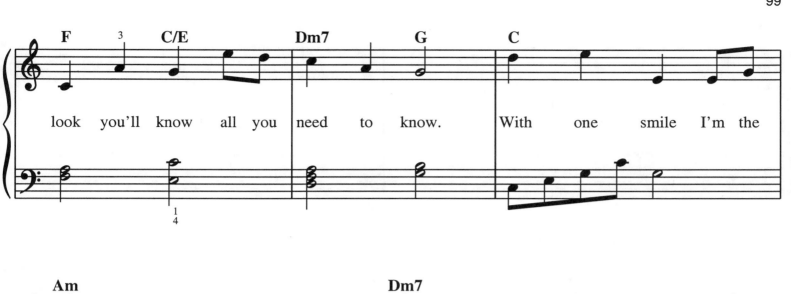

look you'll know all you need to know. With one smile I'm the

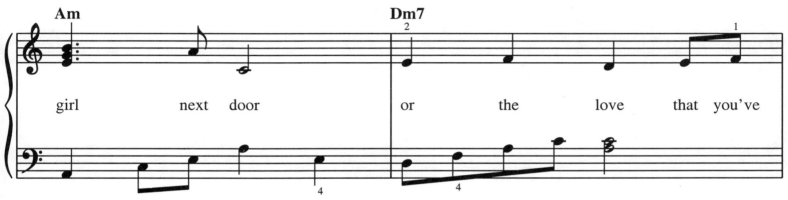

girl next door or the love that you've

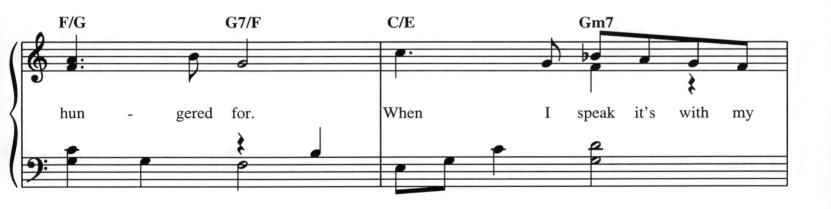

hun - gered for. When I speak it's with my

soul I can play an - y role. No

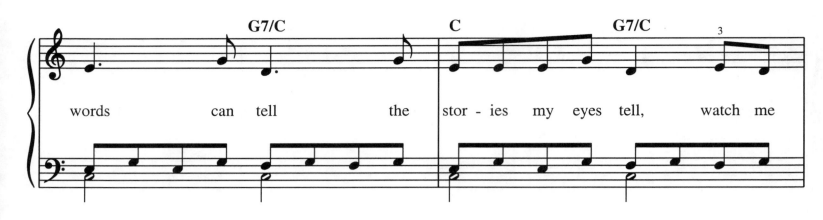

words can tell the stor - ies my eyes tell, watch me

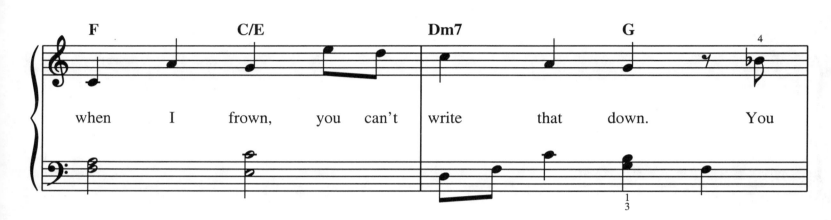

when I frown, you can't write that down. You

know I'm right, it's there in black and white, when I

look your way you'll hear what I say. Yes, with one look I put